THE STUDY OF THE HISTORY OF MATHEMATICS

and

THE STUDY OF THE HISTORY OF SCIENCE

(Two volumes bound as one.)

by

George Sarton

DOVER PUBLICATIONS, INC.

NEW YORK

CONSTABLE & CO LTD
10-12 ORANGE STREET, LONDON, W.C.2

THE STUDY OF THE HISTORY OF MATHEMATICS

by

George Sarton

DOVER PUBLICATIONS, INC.
NEW YORK

Preface to the Dover Edition

I am grateful to Dover Publications for issuing, at a relatively low price, new editions of these two little books of mine which have long been out of print. Each of them contains two parts: first, a text explaining the meaning of the history of science (or the history of mathematics) and, second, a bibliography facilitating additional studies. These bibliographies are not up-to-date but contain the essential down to time of first publication. Readers who are sufficiently inquisitive will be able to complete them easily by referring to my book *Horus, A Guide to the History of Science,* published by Chronica Botanica, Waltham, Mass., in 1952. But even that is not absolutely up-to-date, for up-to-dateness in an evanescent quality in a world changing as fast as ours. Readers wanting the very latest information on the history of science should consult regularly in a public library, or better still at home, the current number of *Isis, An International Quarterly Review devoted to the History of Science,* edited by I. Bernard Cohen, Widener Library 189, Cambridge 38, Mass.

The main thing is to understand that in a world dominated by scientific methods and inventions the history of science should be the keystone of higher education.

Christmas 1954   GEORGE SARTON

CONTENTS

THE STUDY OF THE HISTORY
OF MATHEMATICS

THE STUDY OF THE HISTORY OF
MATHEMATICS

THE remarks which I have made on another occasion with reference to the history of science [1] would apply equally well to the history of mathematics; there is no need of repeating them. However, the history of any special science suggests new considerations. As long as the history of science was conceived as the sum of the histories of special sciences, the relationship between the former and the latter was simple enough. The history of each special science was simply a part of a whole; a part which could easily be removed and isolated. However, that old Whewellian conception had to be abandoned, as it was borne in gradually upon scholars that one of the most valuable aspects of the history of science was the study of the interrelationships between different branches and their mutual enrichment. The history of science could no longer be conceived as a sum of particular histories, but rather as an organic integration, whence no part could be abstracted without damage. Moreover the history of each science is necessarily more technical than that of science as a whole, more concerned with scientific than with cultural continuity. As it deals with a more limited group of ideas it can hope to follow these more closely. To be sure, these differences are quantitative rather than qualitative, and would vary considerably from one historian to another. The one might write a history of science of a very abstract type; the other, a history, say, of chemistry, which would contain fewer technicalities than humanities. In general, however, we should expect the opposite.

[1] G. Sarton, *The Study of the History of Science, with an Introductory Bibliography* (Cambridge, Harvard University Press, 1936). See also *The History of Science Versus the History of Medicine* (*Isis*, vol. 23, pp. 313–320, 1935).

The history of mathematics is essentially different from the history of other sciences in its relationship with the history of science, because it never was an integral part of the latter in the Whewellian sense. The reason for this is obvious: mathematics being far more esoteric than the other sciences, its history can only be told to a select group of initiates. It is true that there are in every science certain questions which are more difficult to explain than others, or cannot be explained without long preliminaries, but those questions are almost exclusively recent ones; in the case of mathematics, on the contrary, the difficulties began very early. There are problems which exercised the minds of men in the fifth century B.C. and cannot be entirely explained to the non-mathematicians of to-day, and it is impossible to make the latter realize the grandeur and beauty of Greek mathematics.

One might thus oppose the history of mathematics to the history of science, and this is often done for practical reasons. The teacher of the history of science being obliged to omit mathematical questions — especially the most interesting ones —, because only a part of his audience could be expected to understand them, it is natural enough to organize separate courses devoted to the history of mathematics. There are then at least two courses (or two series of courses) completing one another, the history of science and the history of mathematics.

It is a pity that this should be so, for the history of mathematics should really be the kernel of the history of culture. Take the mathematical developments out of the history of science, and you suppress the skeleton which supported and kept together all the rest. Mathematics gives to science its innermost unity and cohesion, which can never be entirely replaced with props and buttresses or with roundabout connections, no matter how many of these may be introduced.

On the other hand, the historian of mathematics, remembering that his activity is complementary to that of the historian of science, will not attempt to do over again the latter's task, and he may even feel inclined to take of his own subject too technical and too narrow a view. Therefore, it is well to insist that he should seize every occasion to indicate the relationships between mathematics and other sciences, and to insist that these relationships have always been reciprocal: mathematical problems being often the result of physical needs, while mathematical elaboration gave physics, and, gradually, other sciences, not only means of discovery of almost miraculous potency, but also perfect models of analysis and synthesis.

Some historians of mathematics, with a strong bent for humanism, are willing to consider not only other scientific activities than the purely mathematical, but the whole gamut of life. So much the better. Others, moving in the opposite direction, feel that the history of mathematics itself — not to speak of the history of science — is too complicated a subject, and, wishing to avoid the endless intricacies of the mathematical tree, they select one branch of it, and study its development in more or less complete isolation from the others. Thus the historian may be led to investigate the development of algebra across the ages, or the amplifications of a single idea, like the idea of number, function, or group.

Such abstraction in historical research, as opposed to the more natural procedure of considering each fact as it occurs in due chronological order, is very arbitrary. It is perhaps worth while to examine the matter a little more carefully. The filiation of ideas is somewhat like the filiation of individuals, except that the intricacy is even greater. Any individual A thinking only of his own genealogy has a simple pattern in his mind like our figure 1, but that pattern is obviously a false one, from every point of view except that of his own unimportant personality. In reality, the pattern is enormously more complicated, for each couple may have had more than one child, each person may have married more than once, and marriages between cousins have introduced new cross-relationships. The complete picture of a man's family is like a network which, if it be drawn completely even for only a few generations, is almost inextricable. Of course there is nothing to prevent any individual from selecting in that network and drawing more

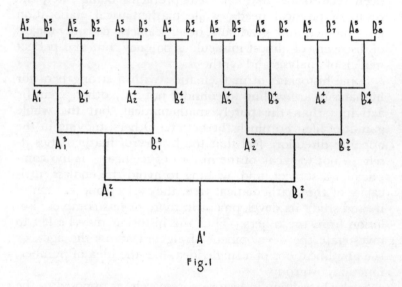

Fig. 1

heavily the lines which concern him immediately, the blood-lines, but the personal pattern thus abstracted from the whole network is of no interest except to himself.

Now the filiation of ideas is necessarily more complicated, for the biological pattern is rigorously limited by the rule that each individual has two parents, neither more nor less, while each idea may result from the fusion of more than two others, or on the contrary may be the fruit of a kind of parthenogenesis. Whenever the historian tries to relate the history of a single group of ideas he is obliged to abstract one pattern from a network of endless complexity, and such an abstraction, however interesting it may be, is always arbitrary to a degree.

The study of special branches of mathematics or of special mathematical ideas is very useful, for it helps one to understand those particular ideas more deeply, but it should not be allowed to confuse our historical perspective. The historian must try to keep in mind the chronological succession not of this or that idea, abstracted from the rest, but of the main ideas, all of them in their mutual relationships and in their diverse connections with the rest of life.

* * *

Many times have I compared the history of science with a secret history, the account of a development taking place mysteriously in the darkness, while the majority of people are more interested and more immediately affected by the events happening on the battlefield or the forum, or by the vicissitudes of their own selves and families. For societies, even as for individuals, one must make a sharp distinction between the things which are the most urgent and those which are the most important. These things are not by any means the same. The most urgent necessity is to live, to remain alive, that is, to eat, sleep, to be happy, to procreate children, and obtain security for one's family. That means physiology, business, and sport, and often enough war. However, the most important things are not to satisfy one's physiological needs, but to increase the cultural heritage which has been bequeathed to us. The urgent things are obvious enough, and men's efforts to obtain them fill the whole historical picture; one can hardly see anything else. Yet all the time some men pursue in the darkness, secretly, the fulfilment of their intellectual desires and of humanity's highest purpose.

If the history of science is a secret history, then the history of mathematics is doubly secret, a secret within a secret, for the growth of mathematics is unknown not only to the general public, but even to scientific workers. It is true, engineers may be found from time to time employing a new formula, but this does not imply any knowledge or understanding of the process which led to it. Even so the average citizen uses every day more and more complicated and marvellous machines about which he knows less and less.

Yet that secret activity is fundamental; it is all the time creating new theories, which sooner or later will set new wheels moving, new machines working, or, better still, will enable us to obtain a deeper understanding of the mechanism of the universe.

The practical man may neglect those *secreta secretorum*, but the philosopher cannot neglect them without loss and without disgrace. The 'practical' and hard-headed mathematician, bent on his own investigations and nothing else, may neglect them too, but he will be a poorer man for doing so. Indeed, one may claim that the history of mathematics provides for him the very best education, the best humanistic initiation, one especially adapted to his own needs.

Let us contemplate for a moment the magnificent panorama of mathematical history as it unfolds itself before us when we evoke the past. First, millenaries of preparation during which some fundamental discoveries are already adumbrated: the idea of number slowly emerges from the darkness, the idea of fraction, the idea of periodicity in geometrical patterns, and others. By the middle of the fourth millennium before Christ, the Egyptians were already acquainted with large numbers of the order of millions, and with a decimal system of numeration. Before the middle of the second millennium they had already attained sufficient geometrical insight to determine the area of any triangle as we do it ourselves, and to solve more difficult problems, such as finding the volume of a frustum of a square pyramid. To measure the area of a circle they squared eight-ninths of its diameter, which was a remarkably good approximation. During all that time the people of Mesopotamia had been developing a mathematics of their own which was as admirable as the Egyptian. In the fourth millennium the Sumerians had already some kind of 'position' concept in the writing of numbers, and had learned to treat submultiples in the same way as multiples, an idea which the Western world did not recapture until fifty centuries later. The geometry of the Babylonians did not reach the same level as that of the Egyptians, but on the other hand their resourcefulness in algebra was astounding, for they succeeded in solving not only quadratic but even cubic equations. To appreciate the relative importance of these achievements it is well to remember that we are much closer to Euclid, often called 'the father of geometry,' than Euclid was to the unknown Egyptian and Mesopotamian mathematicians.

In reality the way for Euclidean mathematics was very gradually and thoroughly prepared, not only by the millenary efforts of Africans and Asiatics, but by three centuries of persistent investigations by the most gifted people among our ancestors, the Greeks of the golden age. The historian is made to witness the building up, as it were stone by stone, of that wonderful monument, geometry, as it was finally transmitted to us in the *Elements*. The Greek 'miracle' continued for at least six more centuries after Euclid, but with less and less intensity and with longer intervals of sleep between the periods of creation. In the meanwhile, the centre of mathematical light had moved from Athens for a brief interval to Syracuse and then to the Greco-oriental city of Alexandria, where it remained for centuries. Thus was their debt to Egypt abundantly repaid by the Greek masters and their Roman disciples.

After the Romans came the barbarians, and ancient wisdom was in danger of complete oblivion, when it was unexpectedly rescued by the Arabs. These were also barbarians, but barbarians redeemed by an intense faith and, for a few centuries at least, by an unquenchable curiosity. The masterpieces of Greek mathematics were translated into Arabic and thus transmitted to the West. If we call the Greek astounding rationalization of geometrical thought a miracle (by means of which word we simply mean to convey that we cannot account for the achievement but only marvel at it), then the Arabic rescue and renaissance was another miracle, that is, a series of events which nobody could have foreseen and which nobody can completely explain.

The Arabs were mainly transmitters and brokers, but their brokerage in a period of crisis was almost providential. They brought together Hindu and Greek ideas, fertilizing the ones with the others, and revolutionizing arithmetic, algebra, and trigonometry. Their own contributions in these branches of mathematics were considerable, and in geometry they were sufficiently good pupils of the Greeks to discuss the postulates of Euclid and solve the most difficult problems of Archimedean and Apollonian geometry at a time when Latin knowledge had sunk below the Egyptian or the Babylonian level. After five centuries of leadership the Arabic culture succumbed under the stress of political vicissitudes and Muslim obscurantism, and a new renaissance of mathematics began in Western Europe.

That Renaissance, slowly prepared by Christian and Jewish mathematicians, blossomed first, as we should expect, in Italy, then in the Netherlands, England, and the other countries of Europe, where trade was flourishing and new cities rapidly growing, where universities vied with one another, and emulation was excited by proud challenges from some of the mathematicians to their rivals. Thus was gradually introduced a second golden age almost as brilliant as the first. Just think of this array of men, the children of a single century: Kepler, Napier, Briggs, Fermat, Descartes, Desargues, Pascal, Huygens, Newton, Leibniz, Seki Kōwa. What could we say of those giants in so brief a sketch as this, except that the glory of Greece, so well known to all of them (except the last), was resurrected in them? In a way they continued the Greek tradition, and they did it with so much fervour that they almost forgot their humbler but very real debts to the Middle Ages. This golden age was not transitory, like the Greek one; it continued, with less splendor perhaps but with equal greatness, until our own days. The immense prestige of the seventeenth-century mathematics is partly due to the effect of contrast. The giants of those golden days seem more gigantic because they rose so near the mediaeval plains. We are startled when we think of the close succession of their achievements, and the cumulative effect upon us is similar to that of the mountains which we see in the course of a journey. As we come from the lowlands, the first snowy peak amazes us, and if many such giants of nature follow each other within a relatively short time we may be completely overwhelmed. There were a number of mathematical giants in the eighteenth and nineteenth centuries, but by that time a new pace had already been set, and one almost expected mathematical progress to continue indefinitely at the same rate.

Will it continue? It is too early to know, but the twentieth century has strongly accentuated the spirit of criticism which characterized the end of the last century, and created in mathematics, as well as in other fields of science, a period of examination, experimentation (yes, even in mathematics),[1] and revolutionary thought, which may be the best preparation for new adventures and new discoveries. We cannot tell what will happen, because such fermentation of mathematical ideas has not occurred before on the same scale: it may be a good omen, or the outcome may be smaller than the bustle. Let us remember the secrecy of mathematics. Great discoveries are not made without preparation, far from it, but they are likely to come in very quietly, without drums and trumpets.

[1] See some excellent remarks on the subject by Pierre Boutroux in his *L'idéal scientifique des mathématiciens* (Paris, 1920), pp. 191, 210.

One thing is certain, the climax of the seventeenth century and that of to-day are not the last ones, though young men may sometimes feel discouraged and think that all the worth-while discoveries have already been made and that nothing remains to be found but odd gleanings. Such a feeling is sometimes induced by the very necessities of their mathematical education. Indeed, dogmatic teaching, even at its best, tends to create an impression of finality which is more satisfying than stimulating. It should appease those young students to realize that such feeling is not by any means new, but has occurred time after time, whenever the intellectual horizon had been suddenly broadened by men of genius. At such times there has been a tendency to see in the latest broadening the final revelation. I am sure some of the old Egyptians of fifty centuries ago felt that way in their moments of despondency: the best had been done, and further progress would become increasingly difficult, if not impossible.

Consider the following example, which is a little closer to us. In the report on mathematical progress prepared for the French Academy of Sciences at Napoleon's request, Delambre remarked:

It would be difficult and perhaps foolhardy to analyze the chances of further progress; in almost every part of mathematics one is stopped by unsurmountable difficulties; improvements in the details seem to be the only possibilities which are left. . . . All these difficulties seem to announce that the power of our analysis is almost exhausted, even as the power of ordinary algebra with regard to transcendental geometry in the time of Leibniz and Newton, and that there is a need of combinations opening a new field to the calculation of transcendental quantities and to the solution of the equations including them.[1]

One cannot help smiling when one bears in /mind the phenomenal mathematical progress which has taken place since 1810, when Delambre made that statement. To be

[1] J. B. J. Delambre, *Rapport historique sur les progrès des sciences mathématiques depuis 1789* (Paris, 1810), p. 99.

sure Delambre was careful in qualifying it: no progress is conceivable unless new combinations are found; but not only were new combinations found, the old ones were far from being used up. Have we not witnessed in recent times an astounding revival of elementary geometry, the new geometry of the triangle and the tetraedron, the circle and the sphere? And yet, such is the incorrigibleness of human nature, a mathematician who has distinguished himself in that very field, Julian Coolidge, has just indulged his own pessimism in a lecture on the rise and fall of projective geometry.[1] If theorems which Euclid might have discovered were not discovered until twenty-two centuries later, may we not assume that Steiner, von Staudt, and their disciples have overlooked more things than we can imagine?

The history of mathematics is exhilarating, because it unfolds before us the vision of an endless series of victories of the human mind, victories without counterbalancing failures, that is, without dishonorable and humiliating ones, and without atrocities. At the same time it helps to dispel pessimism. However great the victories may be, the seasoned historian expects still more and greater ones. Has it not always been so? Has not each mathematical conquest been followed with another and nobler one? History shows that time after time a theory which was thought final and complete was nothing but a stepping stone to a better one, and new theories were thus established one after another when there seemed to be no more room for them. Why should the future be essentially different from the past? Why should our presence to-day create such a strange discontinuity in human evolution? It is thus highly probable that mathematics will continue to be unfolded with greater and greater exuberance. There may be now and then periods of rest and fallow, but it is almost inconceivable that our knowledge should ever be everywhere lost and permanently

---

[1] *American Mathematical Monthly*, vol. 41, pp. 217–228 (1934); cf. *Isis*, vol. 23, p. 582.

stopped. It cannot decrease, it is bound to increase, though no one can foretell the rate of growth.

The process of growing abstraction, diversity, and complexity which began in prehistoric days when the idea of number was adumbrated, and which has never since been completely checked, will continue. There is no reason why it should not. The mathematical field has been enormously enlarged, it is true, but the larger the field, the greater, not smaller, are the opportunities; the longer the frontiers of science, the more space there is for new departures into the unknown. On the basis of my historical experience, I fully believe that mathematics of the twenty-fifth century will be as different from that of to-day as the latter is from that of the sixteenth century.

In the meanwhile, our intellectual wealth is becoming truly embarrassing. The mathematical universe is already so large and diversified that it is hardly possible for a single mind to grasp it, or, to put it in another way, so much energy would be needed for grasping it that there would be none left for creative research. A mathematical congress of to-day reminds one of the Tower of Babel, for few men can follow profitably the discussions of sections other than their own, and even there they are sometimes made to feel like strangers. In consequence, the explorer and the conqueror are condemned to relative ignorance and blindness, and they become less and less able to complete their task without guidance from others. This illustrates in another way the increasing need of mathematical surveys, historical analyses, philosophical elaborations.

* * *

No thinking man can contemplate the mathematical past without asking himself some fundamental questions, which are as simple to formulate as they are difficult to answer. To what extent were the filiation and development of ideas determined either by outside circumstances or by a kind of internal necessity? An extreme answer to that question was suggested by Évariste Galois:

La science progresse par une série de combinaisons où le hazard ne joue pas le moindre rôle; sa vie est brute et ressemble à celle des minéraux qui croissent par juxtà position. Celà s'applique non seulement à la science telle qu'elle résulte des travaux d'une série de savants, mais aussi aux recherches particulières à chacun d'eux. En vain les analystes voudraient-ils se le dissimuler: ils ne déduisent pas, ils combinent, ils comparent; quand ils arrivent à la vérité, c'est en heurtant de côté et d'autre qu'il y sont tombés.[1]

There is no doubt that Galois's curious answer was itself dominated by an internal necessity, by the merciless genius in him which left him no choice but to obey. He must have felt strongly the hopelessness of resisting one's fate. As to external necessities, very clear answers on the subject have been given us repeatedly by mathematicians of the new Russian persuasion. According to them, even Newton's achievement was conditioned by the economic needs of his time. And yet I am not convinced. It is easy enough to explain some facts retrospectively, especially if one be free to select the convenient facts and to abandon the inconvenient ones. Why did the most industrial and mercantile nation of Europe reject the metric system, while its use would have caused great economies in time and money? Suppose the situation had been reversed, how tempting it would have been to explain the creation of the metric system as a necessary result of the superior mercantilism of England.

There is no doubt that mathematical discoveries are conditioned by outside events of every kind, political, economic, scientific, military, and by the incessant demands of the arts of peace and war. Mathematics did never develop in a political or economic vacuum. However, we think that those events were only some of the factors among others,

---

[1] From Mss. edited by Jules Tannery in *Bulletin des sciences mathématiques*, vol. 41, p. 260 (1906), Galois's spelling being preserved. Galois's other remarks are well worth reading; they are brilliant and inconsistent. See below.

factors the power of which might vary and did vary from time to time. It might be almost decisive in one case, and ineffectual in another.

Even the internal necessity, though much stronger than the external one, might be inoperative. While the properties of ellipses were revealed in the second half of the third century B.C. by the genius of Apollonios, astronomers continued for more than eighteen centuries to account for the erratic motions of the planets by complicated systems of epicycles and eccentrics. Granted that the problem of finding the earth's trajectory was exceedingly difficult,[1] Kepler's achievement might have occurred much earlier. One would have thought that the concept of the ellipse would have been strong enough to impose itself on men's minds and to find for itself beautiful applications.

The historian is unable to dictate how things will happen or should happen; he must be satisfied to describe humbly enough how they did happen. He naturally tries to arrange events in causal sequences, but he should never indulge in dogmatism on the subject.

The main sources of mathematical invention seem to be within man rather then outside of him: his own inveterate and insatiable curiosity, his constant itching for intellectual adventure; and likewise the main obstacles to mathematical progress seem to be also within himself; his scandalous inertia and laziness, his fear of adventure, his need of conformity to old standards, and his obsession by mathematical ghosts. It is true these ghosts may sometimes suggest valuable applications and survive. For example, the shadow of the unitary fractions of the Egyptians influenced mathematics for centuries and impeded its progress, but they suggested incidentally the *fractiones in gradibus* of Leonardo Fibonacci (1202) and the continued fractions of later times.[2]

---

[1] See Einstein's remarks on this in *Comment je vois le monde* (Paris, 1934), pp. 173–180; cf. *Isis*, vol. 23, pp. 278–280.

[2] Ettore Bortolotti, "La propagation de la science à travers les siècles," in *Scientia*, vol. 52, supplement, pp. 133–146 (1932).

Our mathematical practice of to-day is still littered with the fossils of earlier times, such as Roman numerals, sexagesimal fractions, the English weights and measures, etc.; on the other hand, other relics have been abandoned, the rediscovery of which delights the historian, even as obsolete curios delight the archaeologist. When we compare the whole of mankind with a single man growing in knowledge and wisdom, we may stretch the comparison a little further: no man remembers equally well everything; even the best memory experiences lapses, betrayals, and preferences. The whole of mankind is like a man with a memory that is good but not perfect.

The deterministic theory of mathematical progress remains insufficient even when one has corrected and tempered it as we have done. It is not always possible to account for the development of mathematical ideas by a combination of external events with personal impulses on the one hand and personal inhibitions on the other, great as is the flexibility of such a method. There are many facts which one cannot account for in a general way, and this applies to mathematical inventions as well as to any other details of human behavior. Many mathematical developments are capricious in the extreme, and it is a waste of time to try to find a rational explanation of them. Strangely enough, in the same text wherein Galois expressed so strongly his belief in mathematical fatality, he also called attention to the great irregularity and disorder of our mathematical knowledge. An orderly development would only be possible for a godlike mathematician knowing in advance all the possible mathematics.

Here is really the crux of the matter. Mathematicians and other scientists, however great they may be, do not know the future. Their genius may enable them to project their purpose ahead of them; it is as if they had a special lamp, unavailable to lesser men, illuminating their path; but even in the most favorable cases the lamp sends only a very small cone of light into the infinite darkness. Enthusiastic admirers of great men often make the mistake of giving them credit for the endless consequences of their discoveries, consequences which they could not possibly foresee. To credit Galois with all the results of the theory of groups is as foolish as to credit Faraday with all. the wonders of electrotechnics, or to hold Columbus responsible for all the good and evil done in the New World since 1492. The founder of a new theory or of a new science deserves full credit for the discoveries which he actually made, less credit for those which he adumbrated, and still less for those which he made possible but did not realize. While we honor him as a founder, we must remember that he could not possibly anticipate all the consequences of his ideas and all the fruits of his deeds. He is the spiritual lord of the domain which his imagination could encompass, neither more nor less. We often call him the father of this or that, and such a term is appropriate enough to express our respect, even our veneration, if we bear in mind that parents should not be praised or blamed too much for their children, though they made them, not to speak of their more distant descendants who sprang from other loins.

The capriciousness of mathematical development cannot be emphasized too much. Why were the early Greeks so interested in the theory of numbers, and so little in plain arithmetic? The latter was highly needed. Every reason of economic necessity should have caused the development of arithmetic, and discouraged as a luxury the growth of fanciful ideas on the properties of numbers. Why did magic squares interest so many peoples East and West? Why? Why? The student of history should not ask such childish queries. His purpose cannot be to give a completely logical account of the past, for such account is obviously out of the question. It is only here and there that a few logical knots can be tied; for the rest, we must be satisfied with a faithful description of the possibilities which materialized among an infinity of others which did not. The shortest distance from one point to another is a geodetic line, but such a line can only be followed if one knows one's destination, in which case there would be no discovery. The ways of discovery must necessarily be very different from the shortest way, indirect and circuitous, with many windings and retreats. It is only at a later stage of knowledge, when a new domain has been sufficiently explored, that it becomes possible to reconstruct the whole theory on a logical basis, and to show how it might have been discovered by an omniscient being, that is, how it might have been discovered if there had been no real need of discovering it! Galois's impatience with the textbooks of his day was inconsistent. It is as if an explorer of an unknown territory complained of the absence of maps, or the student of an unknown language of the lack of grammars and dictionaries.

To conclude, capriciousness is of the essence of discovery, because we can only know where we are going, and whether it is worth going to, when we are there. Accordingly we cannot help following many false trails, and going astray in many ways. Moreover, caprice is of the essence of life in general, and of human life in particular, because of life's very complexity and indetermination.

* * *

Nevertheless, the development of mathematics is perhaps less capricious than that of other sciences, more completely determined (or less undetermined), if not by external factors, at least by internal ones, for each theory presses forward as it were, and the mathematicians who are playing with it must needs perceive some of its consequences. The desire to follow them to the limit is then likely to prove irresistible, whether these consequences be useful or not. The concatenations of mathematical ideas are not divorced from life, far from it, but they are less influenced than other scientific ideas by accidents, and it is perhaps more possible, and more permissible, for a mathematician than for any other man to secrete himself in a tower of ivory.

* * *

The history of mathematics is thus a good field for the investigation of theories concerning the progress of science in general, and the possibilities of logical development in particular. It is conceivable that the capriciousness is only relative after all, that it affects the details of the picture rather than the main outline. Such a conception is attractive enough to be fully investigated, and only the historian can do it. The vicissitudes of history might be overlooked in a first approximation. One might assume that Man (not this man or that, whatever be his genius) followed unerringly the geodetic line from A to B (A and B being two mathematical discoveries) instead of meandering and beating about the bush (fig. 2).

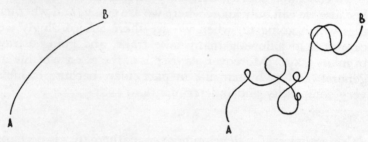

Fig. 2

This assumption, in fact, the historian of mathematics is often obliged to make, if only for the sake of brevity and simplicity. Reality is far too complex to be represented to the last detail, but the historian's simplification must remain sufficiently close to it; it must represent the main outline in chronological sequence. It is thus exceedingly different from the synthetic reconstruction made by teachers, wherein the chronological sequence is necessarily disregarded as irrelevant. The mathematician whose privilege it is to give to a theory its final, 'classical' shape, is likely to define the function he is dealing with by means of the property which was perhaps the last one to be discovered. That is all right: the synthesis thus created, however distant it may be from historical contingencies, is closer to the deeper mathematical realities.

We need equally the two kinds of synthesis: the historical and the purely mathematical. The latter is the shortest if not always the easiest path to knowledge, but it fails to explain the human implications; it may satisfy the matter-of-fact and hurried mathematician; it cannot satisfy the philosopher and the humanist.

As to the pure mathematician, even he should not be too easily satisfied with the latest synthesis. To begin with, that synthesis may be incomplete. Some elements which were not deemed essential for it may have other values, they may prove to be essential for other structures, or the one from which they were eliminated may not be as final as it seems. Indeed, no theory is ever final. A new discovery, a new point of view may cause its abandonment and its supersedure by another, and the facts neglected in one shuffling may be considered invaluable in another. Every synthesis implies sacrifices; it is not merely a simplification but also and unavoidably a betrayal of reality, a distortion of the truth, and the mathematician who takes the trouble of considering the origin and evolution of ideas, as well as their final shape, will improve his understanding of them and enrich his mind.

The study of history may, or may not, help the mathematician to make new discoveries by suggesting new connections between old ideas or new applications of old methods; in any case it will complete his mastery of the subject, and provide him with new opportunities for a deeper and more intuitive grasp of it.

* * *

The main reason for studying the history of mathematics, or the history of any science, is purely humanistic. Being men, we are interested in other men, and especially in such men as have helped us to fulfil our highest destiny. As soon as we realize the great part played by individual men in mathematical discoveries — for, however these may be determined, they cannot be brought about except by means of human brains —, we are anxious to know all their circumstances.[1] How did it happen that this man or that man, among others, was devoted to mathematics? Was he thus consecrated before being conscious of it, or did he consecrate himself? How did his mathematical genius assert itself, how did it blossom out? Was it hard for him or easy? Did he succeed in establishing his theories and convincing his contemporaries of their importance? All these questions and many others are deeply interesting, especially for other mathematicians: if they are young, because of their dreams of the future and their hopes and doubts; if they are older, because of their memories of the past, and also, though in a different way, because of their hopes and doubts.

One soon realizes that mathematicians are much like other men, except in the single respect of their special genius, and that that genius itself has many shapes and aspects. I remember reading in John Addington Symonds's biography this portrait of a great musician:

Here was a man Handel, a fat native of Halle, in the Duchy of Magdeburg, articled at eight years old to an organist, and from that moment given up to music — a man who never loved a woman, who (to use the

---

[1] Such inquisitiveness may seem idle to those relatively few men who are too engrossed in their own thoughts to care for anything else, but it represents one of the oldest human instincts. The same instinct reveals itself on a lower level through the immense curiosity concerning murders. Newspapers are skilful in pandering to such curiosity to their own profit. Even as the mass of the people are insatiable in their desire to know every detail of a murder case, so those who are more thoughtful wish to investigate every detail of scientific discoveries or other creative achievements.

words of his enthusiastic biographer) continued irritable, greedy, fond of solitude, persevering, unaffectionate, coarse and garrulous in conversation, benevolent, independent, fond of beer, religious, without passions, and without a single intellectual taste. He had never received any education except in counterpoint. He had had no experience. Yet he could interpret the deepest psychological secrets; he could sing dithyrambs to God, or preach moral sermons; he could express the feelings of mighty nations, and speak with the voice of angels more effectually than even Milton; he could give life to passion, and in a few changes of his melody lead love through all its variations from despair to triumph — there was nothing that he did not know. The whole world had become for him music, and his chords were co-extensive with the universe. Raphael's capability to paint the school of Athens, after coming from the workshop of Perugino, was perhaps less marvellous than Handel's to delineate the length and breadth and height and depth of human nature in his choruses. We shall never comprehend, *nous autres*, the mysteries of genius. It is a God-sent clairvoyance, inexplicable, and different in kind from intellect.[1]

This account has recurred to me almost every time I have been introduced to an original scientist, for it applies to him as well as to his musical brethren.

The great mathematician may be a man of very limited experience and wisdom outside his own field and his advice in non-mathematical matters may be of very little value; he may be burdened with all kinds of passions and weaknesses; in short, he is like the rest of us except in one essential respect. When we write his biography it is clear that it is that essential thing, his genius, which must remain in the centre of the picture, but our curiosity does not stop there. We may be so deeply interested in his personality that we desire to know everything, whether good or bad, which concerns it. That is all right. Full and honest biographies should be encouraged by all means, they help us to know our fellow men and ourselves better, but that loathsome fashion of our time, which is called 'debunking' — the dragging down of great men to the level of their

---

[1] John Addington Symonds, as quoted by Horatio F. Brown in the latter's biography of him (London, 1895, 2 vols.), vol. I, pp. 343–344.

meretricious biographers — should be discouraged. It is a matter of measure. It is very well to show all the weaknesses of a hero, but this should be subordinated to the main purpose, the description of his genius, the explanation of the discoveries which it made possible, the contemplation of the truth and beauty which it revealed.

For example, a great mathematician may be a drunkard, for his mind's obsession with mathematical ideas may sometimes become unendurable, a real torture from which he may wish to escape. Drink may provide a welcome relief; if in addition his will be feeble — and there is no reason why genius should always be associated with a will strong enough to cope with it —, and if he be afflicted with sorrows, he may become an habitual tippler and disgrace himself accordingly. Such facts should not be hidden by the biographer, but they should not be unduly magnified by him. Our hero does not become more 'human' and more lovable because he is shown to be a drunkard, though we may feel much sympathy for him in his troubles; and, of course, his genius is not at all explained by his drunkenness. Such a detail, we should remember, is interesting, but only in its proper place, the dim background; to insist upon it or to focus the picture upon it is a cruel distortion of the truth. Everybody can get drunk, but the number of mathematicians is small, and the number of creative mathematicians exceedingly small. It is easy enough to cause physical intoxication, but there is no known method for producing that kind of sacred intoxication out of which discoveries bubble.

Mediocre people will perhaps assert that it is now too late for discoveries, that all those of any value have already been made. I have already disposed of this fallacy. It is safer to assume, as a first approximation, that mathematical progress is a function of the size of the mathematical field and of the length of the mathematical frontiers. However it is arguable that the number of great mathematicians does not increase very much from time to time, or does not continue to increase as much as one might expect. It is quite certain that the number of original mathematicians has not increased in proportion to the number of well trained mathematicians, or to the availabilities for mathematical research. This confirms my theory that mathematical theory is not very much determined by external circumstances. The main factor is the availability of creative genius, which cannot be controlled.

In the experimental sciences, discoveries may become possible or be facilitated by the use of new instruments, and in certain cases it is difficult to separate the virtues of the instrument from those of the observer. In mathematics, as in music, genius can be contemplated in a greater state of purity, and hence the history of mathematics is perhaps more interesting to the psychologist than that of any other science.

* * *

To the educated and intelligent mathematician, or at least to the one whose curiosity and intelligence extend beyond the boundaries of his special studies, the history of mathematics affords a recreation which is pleasant as well as instructive. It requires from him no real effort, but he should always remember with gratitude that his enjoyment is made possible by the devotion of a few scholars for whom this is not a pure recreation but a vocation as imperative and tyrannical as his own. Above all, he should bear in mind that history has no value unless it be accurate, or as accurate as possible, and that such accuracy is as difficult to obtain and to increase in this field as in any other. He should insist on being given for his recreation the best and purest kind of history, and not be satisfied with the second best or the imperfect; he should reject without hesitation the books wherein the sober truth is replaced by flippancy and jesting; he should appreciate the efforts made by his scholarly brethren to provide accurate results, or at least he should not throw spokes into their wheels.

* * *

Students of the history of mathematics should try, like the students of other scientific subjects, to be as well acquainted as possible with the relevant literature. This requires patient and sustained efforts, but it is in the end more economical than the duplication of work already done or the utilization of writings already superseded, two wasteful procedures which are the penalties of bibliographic ignorance or negligence.

Nevertheless, the bibliography of a subject should be investigated with moderation and remain a means rather than an end. There are occasions when bibliographical research may be carried on more deeply, for example, when those investigations imply special difficulties, as in the case of oriental manuscripts, but these exceptions should not become the rule. Bibliographical extravagance is a sin rather than a virtue, a real perversity; it is the fruit of pedantry, or if not, it must inevitably lead to it. Whenever the knowledge of a subject is sacrificed to a knowledge of its bibliography we may be sure that there is something wrong with the author, and his bibliographical results deserve less confidence than if he had devoted more time to the study of the subject itself and less to the bibliography of it. Indeed, such immoderate scholars give up precious realities for shadows; they make one think of the fools who to the delusive hope of wealth sacrifice all that makes life worth living.

It is relatively easy to compile enormous lists of titles concerning almost any subject, but such lists are more bewildering than useful if they are not accompanied with critical notes indicating the intrinsic value of each item. Such notes cannot be written by the mere bibliographer, but only by the genuine student of the subject, and the deeper and more original his study, the more reliable will be his appreciation of the work of other people.

* * *

Bibliographical perversion is only an example of a larger category. When investigations become very technical, there is always a danger that the subject be sacrificed to the technique. The best way to minimize this danger is never to lose sight of the purpose of our studies. The purpose cannot be merely to exhibit one's mastery of a difficult technique, but rather to apply that technique to the attainment of a deeper understanding of mathematics and a better appreciation of the humanities implied.

The well tempered historian must beware equally of pedantry on the one hand and of inaccuracy or premature generalization on the other. He must ever bear in mind that, however desirable historical knowledge may be, its value, like that of any other kind of knowledge, is a function of its accuracy. Inaccurate knowledge, that is, knowledge which is below the level of attainable accuracy, is not only worthless; its value is negative.

There has been much discussion in recent years anent the double standard of morality applying to men and women. We are now beginning to realize that what is wrong and dishonorable for a woman is equally wrong and dishonorable for a man. There now remains to be overthrown another double standard of morality which poisons our intellectual atmosphere. Accuracy has the same meaning in history as in science. The scientist who has two standards of truth, one for his scientific work, the other for his historical work, should not be allowed to discredit our studies but only himself. No matter what his 'scientific' reputation may be, as opposed to his 'historical' one, he should be revealed in his true colors, as an incompetent scholar, or a dishonest one, or both, as one who debases our knowledge and defiles his own temple.

The main duty of the historian of mathematics, as well as his fondest privilege, is to explain the humanity of mathematics, to illustrate its greatness, beauty, and dignity, and to describe how the incessant efforts and the accumulated genius of many generations have built up that magnificent monument, the object of our most legitimate pride as men, and of our wonder, humility, and thankfulness as individuals. The study of the history of mathematics will not make better mathematicians but gentler ones, it will enrich their minds, mellow their hearts, and bring out their finer qualities.

NOTE ON THE STUDY OF THE HISTORY
OF MODERN MATHEMATICS

BY 'modern mathematics' is meant roughly mathematics in the nineteenth and twentieth centuries, with special reference to the more difficult parts of it. It is necessary to make such a distinction for almost every branch of science, but above all for mathematics. The more immediate past of mathematics cannot be explored with profit except by a professional mathematician, preferably by one who is familiar with the latest developments of the many questions of which he is trying to reconstruct the evolution.

In a general course on the history of mathematics it is difficult to give a sufficient account of modern mathematics, and if the course is short (as mine is, some thirty-five lectures) it is impossible. Indeed, the growth of mathematics during the last century and a half has been enormous, amazing, and some of the new developments are so esoteric that they cannot be understood by every mathematician, but only by those having undergone a special training in the proper direction.

To illustrate the bewildering complexity of modern mathematics it will suffice to recall the late Florian Cajori's estimate.[1] It took Moritz Cantor four large volumes (about 4000 pages) to tell the history of mathematics from the beginnings to 1799. Cajori calculated that in order to write the history of nineteenth-century mathematics on the same scale some fourteen or fifteen additional volumes would be needed. I have not very much confidence in Cajori's estimate. Modern history should never be written with the same completeness as ancient history, for the simple reason that the sifting of materials, which has been done mercilessly

[1] "Plans for a History of Mathematics in the Nineteenth Century," in *Science*, vol. 48, pp. 279–284 (1918).

by time in the case of the distant past, must be done by the historian with equal severity in the case of the immediate past, or otherwise the real scale is not at all the same. As only a fraction of the ancient mathematical writings have escaped destruction, any fragment, however insignificant, is very valuable, while for modern mathematics our task must be, on the contrary, to eliminate the great majority of the available writings and consider only a few. Every ancient mathematician whose name has come down to us must be dealt with, while for modern ones we need speak only of a small minority of those whom we know. To use another comparison, the map of a fertile and populous country should not be drawn in the same way as that of a desert. The past was not originally a desert, far from it, but it has become one because the vicissitudes of time have obliterated most of its vestiges. Therefore, I think that Cajori's estimate ought to be reduced, but even so the history of modern mathematics could not be tolerably complete without occupying much space.

However, the main difficulty in the teaching of the history of modern mathematics lies not in the richness and exuberance of the subject, but in its technicality. The students attending a general course could not be expected to be sufficiently prepared for the understanding of each lecture. It would be necessary to explain the subject as well as the history of the subject, and this would soon prove impossible.

On the other hand, it seems to be the duty of instructors teaching special subjects to explain their history. For example, consider the teaching of the theory of elliptic functions. Would not the most natural way of introducing that teaching be to explain by what series of circumstances those functions were recognized, how their study forced itself gradually upon the attention of geometers, how it grew by leaps and bounds within the analytic domain, how it branched off and connected itself, little by little, with other branches of mathematics? Thus the course would naturally begin with one or two historical lectures, and if the teacher had the historical sense, he would easily contrive, as the theory unfolded itself, to introduce the main creators: Fagnano, Euler, Lagrange, Legendre, Gauss, Abel, Jacobi, Clebsch, Kronecker, Halphen, Hermite. Please note that if he did that part of his task well enough, if he succeeded in evoking those great personalities, his audience would become familiar with some of the leading mathematicians of the last century. It would be merely a cross-section of nineteenth-century mathematics, but it would be a magnificent cross-section. Every subject taught in our universities to advanced students, theory of surfaces, theory of probabilities, projective geometry, general theory of functions, theory of potential, analysis situs, and so on, would lead to historical cross-sections of a similar kind, and the student guided in such courses by imaginative and historically-minded teachers would begin to have a fair idea of the achievements of the last century. Laplace would not be for him simply the name of a function or an equation, but a man, a man of flesh and blood, a man of towering genius yet as full of vanities as himself; and the same applies to all the names which have become indissolubly attached to mathematical ideas.

In short, the history of modern mathematics should be taught by mathematical teachers in the course of their ordinary teaching, while the history of older mathematics can be properly taught only by a specialist, who must be as much of a historian as of a mathematician, if not more.

Before dropping this part of the subject, let me still add that the professional historian of mathematics is generally unable to see the details of modern mathematics, and especially of the twentieth-century mathematics, in their proper perspective. He is always in danger of not seeing the wood for the trees, and of appreciating incorrectly the relative weight of different facts and theories. Judging from my experience of the past, men are seldom able to measure their contemporaries; they overvalue this one and undervalue the other, and posterity is frequently obliged to correct their conclusions. Why should it be otherwise now? Men are not intrinsically wiser; even if they were, their ability to foresee the future would always be very limited, and in the last analysis, every theory is judged by its fruits, that is, by events which are unknown to the contemporaries. Indeed, one of the sacred duties of historians is to correct the erroneous judgment of the old contemporaries, and give honor where honor is due, especially when it was withheld.

If the teaching of the history of modern mathematics is necessarily restricted, there is no reason why the mathematician should not study it by himself. In fact, there are many good reasons for his doing so. The mathematician's position with regard to history is almost the reverse of the historian's, for the field he is best prepared for is modern mathematics, while the investigation of ancient mathematics is probably beyond his ability.

Generally speaking, mathematicians can hardly be expected to take an active interest in historical research. Not only do they lack time for it, but mathematical creation is of its nature tyrannical and exclusive; it is difficult, if not impossible, for the creative mathematician to give much thought to anything else, least of all to history, which involves an intellectual effort of an absolutely different kind.

However, he may be obliged to investigate earlier writings in the very domain he is exploring, and this may lead him into historical interludes of greater or lesser frequency according to the particular constitution of his own mind. Thus a man like Klein ended in giving considerable time and thought to historical matters without ever ceasing to be a creative mathematician of the first order.

There is no doubt that a very large amount of work remains to be done, which can be done only by historically-minded mathematicians rather than by mathematically-minded historians. Furthermore, it is only when much of that work has been done, that is, when a great many analyses and partial syntheses of various kinds have been accomplished, that it will become at all possible to write the history of modern mathematics which Florian Cajori had in mind.

* * *

The following remarks concern chiefly the mathematician who may be induced to do from time to time some of this historical, or semi-historical, work. The purely technical difficulties on the historical side are small, incomparably smaller than in the case of ancient, mediaeval, or oriental mathematics, where they tend to predominate, but that does not mean that they do not exist. There are many pitfalls, no less dangerous because of their apparent insignificance.

The dating of discoveries is much easier, of course, than in earlier times, especially in times anterior to printing, but the dating must be more precise. Discoveries were often made almost simultaneously by different authors, and it may be necessary to determine the priority of one of them, and the dependence of the others on him, or, on the contrary, their independence from him. Controversies over priority can only be settled by very accurate dating of the rival achievements. The dates printed on books and on fascicles of periodicals may not be reliable, or if reliable, they may not be sufficiently accurate.

The date of the reading of a paper before an academy or scientific society is sometimes considered as the date of publication, but this is very misleading. For the reading may never have taken place, and even if it took place, it was in all probability fragmentary and incomplete, and there is nothing to guarantee that the paper actually published a year or many years later is identical with the one which was 'read.' [1] On the contrary, the chances are that the author improved his paper in the meanwhile by omission or commission, by various changes or interpolations, and he may have availed himself of new ·discoveries almost until the eleventh hour.

A good illustration of this is provided by Hamilton's memoirs on the mathematical development of the wave theory of light, which appeared from 1827 to 1833 in the *Transactions* of the Royal Irish Academy.[2] The last of these papers, 'read' before the Academy in October, 1832, contained his famous prediction of conical refraction. This was verified experimentally by Lloyd on December 14, and his verification was reported to the Academy on January 28, 1833. Hamilton's and Lloyd's memoirs were published in the same number of the *Transactions* in the summer of 1833. Now Hamilton's memoir, assumedly 'read in October, 1832,' contains the law of conical polarization subsequently discovered by Lloyd, without reference to him. This was done without intention to deceive; the facts were so well known to other members of the Academy that definite acknowledgments seemed unnecessary. However, on the basis of Hamilton's publication 'read in October, 1832' the priority of the discovery of the law of conical polarization might be ascribed by a careless historian to Hamilton, while it truly belongs to Lloyd.

This is not an exceptional case. The same sequence of events is likely to have happened more than once, and, be it noted, more often than not without dishonesty. Each scientist is naturally anxious that his paper should be up-

---

[1] There are exceptions to this, the most remarkable being the *Comptes rendus hebdomadaires des séances de l'Académie des Sciences*, founded by Arago in 1835. The Académie meets every Monday (or sometimes Tuesday) of every week of the year, without vacation; the *Comptes rendus* appearing every Saturday contain the extracts of the papers actually read on the preceding Monday.

[2] G. Sarton, "Discovery of Conical Refraction by William Rowan Hamilton and Humphrey Lloyd, 1833," in *Isis*, vol. 17, pp. 154–170 (1932).

to-date when it appears, he will correct it up to the last minute, and take advantage of his discussion of it with colleagues and of every ulterior publication as far as possible.

The dates printed on the covers of periodicals are often inaccurate. Such errors are notorious to contemporaries, at least to those who trouble to compare the printed dates with the dates of reception, but the discrepancy soon ceases to be perceptible and is readily forgotten.

The account of their discoveries given by mathematicians — as well as by other scientists — should never be accepted without control. A scientist may falsify that account, consciously or unconsciously. Conscious falsifications are probably rare, at least in modern times, but the unconscious ones may be frequent, and the more misleading because of their ingenuity. The discoverer may be unconsciously led to exaggerate the difficulties, to minimize his own hesitations; his remembrance of various circumstances may be strangely garbled, and his final story as untrue, yet as innocent, as that of any honest angler reporting his feats. He may also antedate his discovery, that is, his initial discovery, which may have been considerably anterior to publication. Such errors, which are psychologically very plausible, increase with the lapse of time, and one must be especially suspicious of them in reminiscences written in old age, often a great many years after the time when the recorded events took place. For an example of such honest misrepresentation, see my paper on Karl Ernst von Baer's discovery of the mammalian ovum; the discovery was made in 1827, his autobiography was written forty years later.[1] This has nothing to do with mathematics, but the example would apply equally well to mathematical discoveries.

The long and the short of it is that the historian must always stand on his guard. 'Seeing is believing' will never do in scientific work. Seeing is not enough, for we often see

[1] G. Sarton, "The Discovery of the Mammalian Egg and the Foundation of Modern Embryology," in *Isis*, vol. 16, pp. 315-378 (1931), especially p. 324.

things which are 'not so,' many statements which have all the appearances of genuineness and authority are nevertheless false, and our own perceptions may need various corrections.

Careless people will say that these errors do not matter. Some of them possibly do not matter, but who can tell, and at any rate, it is not for us, upon whose shoulders the responsibility lies, to decide whether they matter or not. Could we have any confidence in a cashier who kept certain accounts very carefully and others less carefully? The historian who is worth his salt will take infinite pains to collect all available evidence, sift the facts, test them, and avoid every conceivable source of error. This will increase his labor considerably, and not necessarily increase his fame, for the average reader will not see the difference anyhow. The historian is impelled to take these pains, and cannot escape taking them, because he aims at perfection and permanence.

Historical studies undertaken by the mathematician may be of diverse kinds. For example, he may study the career of a man, his mathematical activities in their relationship not only to contemporary mathematics but to the other events of his life, his environment, the influences to which he was exposed or which he exerted, and so forth. The biographical approach is always fascinating, and it may have some heuristic value, that is, good biographies may help young men to find new thoughts or to find themselves, which is hardly less important. Or else the mathematician may investigate the evolution of a definite idea, or group of ideas, choosing, of course, the ideas which he is engaged with himself. Or he may be interested in retracing the history of mathematical activities in a given country or locality, in his own college for instance, or his native town or his home country. Each of these kinds of studies implies different qualities, in addition to the mathematical preparation, which is always a condition *sine qua non*. The other qualifications are less obvious and less imperative, but hardly less important. No one can write a good biography who lacks imagination, insight, and sympathy; he must be able to recapture the feelings and the moods as well as the trains of thought of his subject. The writing of a monograph on the genesis and development of an idea, 'the biography of an idea,' requires a deeper insight into mathematical interrelations and continuities, rather than humanism, yet the account will be more appealing if all the human circumstances and idiosyncrasies which moved the idea now in this, now in that direction are brought out in bold relief against the technical and impersonal background. In many cases the biographical and scientific accounts are interwoven.

The mathematician who has historical leanings should exercise himself in sundry ways, and attempt syntheses of various kinds: vertical (the evolution of an idea or of a man), horizontal (the knowledge attained at a certain time and place). Thus will he gradually master his subject, not only in its present stage, but in its very growth and life and in the continuities and implications of the whole past.

* * *

Historical results are unavoidably incomplete and imperfect, but if we try at all to obtain some of them we should do our very best, and make it unnecessary for others to do our work over again within the near future. Accurate work may seem very expensive in time and energy, but in the long run it is much cheaper than quick and slovenly work, for the latter is worthless. The past to be explored is limited, and is represented to-day by a limited number of documents, some of which are already available, while others are still undiscovered. The total number of those documents can decrease by loss, or destruction, it cannot possibly increase. Hence the investigation of that knowledge is also limited, and, in theory at least, it should be possible to complete it.

That distant aim should be ours. The speed of our work is far less important than its quality. As long as we come nearer to the goal, whether slowly or not, we are doing our share, while the inaccurate and dishonest writers simply pull us back and undo the work already done. They are truly betrayers of our destiny.

The historically-minded mathematician of our time should analyze, sift, and classify the documents of the last century, prepare a number of partial syntheses, and thus facilitate the transmission to our descendants of those treasures of knowledge and humanity, and make possible the broader and deeper syntheses of the future.

BIBLIOGRAPHY OF THE HISTORY
OF MATHEMATICS

BIBLIOGRAPHY OF THE HISTORY OF MATHEMATICS

In spite of its deliberate brevity, this bibliography is so arranged as to enable intelligent students to complete it to any extent. In the meanwhile it will satisfy their immediate needs. They should consult also the bibliography appended to my *Study of the History of Science*, a companion volume to this one. The present bibliography is divided as follows:

I. General treatises, and other works completing them, with regard to the history of mathematics in Egypt, Mesopotamia, Greece, India, the Far East, and in mediaeval times.

II. Handbooks.

III. Treatises devoted to the history of special branches of mathematics. Generalities. Arithmetic. Theory of numbers. Algebra. Determinants. Trigonometry. Elementary geometry. Analytical geometry. Descriptive geometry. Synthetic geometry. Non-Euclidean geometry. Analysis. Calculus of variations. Theory of probabilities.

IV. Mathematics in the nineteenth and twentieth centuries.

V. Philosophy and methodology.

VI. Bibliography. A. Guides. B. Encyclopaedias. C. Large catalogues. D. Journals.

VII. Journals on the history of mathematics.

VIII. Centres of research. A. Academies of science. B. Mathematical societies. C. International congresses. D. Institutes and libraries.

Appendix. Biographies of modern mathematicians.

I. GENERAL TREATISES

Of the early treatises only one deserves to be quoted here.

Jean Étienne Montucla (1725–99), *Histoire des mathématiques* (Paris, 1758, 2 vols). New edition completed by Jérôme de Lalande (1732–1807) (Paris, 1799–1802, 4 vols.).

Especially valuable for the seventeenth and eighteenth centuries; deals not only with mathematics, but with astronomy, and with mathematical and physical sciences in general.. For more details see G. Sarton, "Montucla" in *Osiris*, vol. 1, pp. 519–567, 2 pls. (1936).

Students of the history of mathematics are fortunate in having at their disposal an elaborate treatise, more elaborate than any other treatise in the whole literature of the history of science. That is,

Moritz Cantor (1829–1920), *Vorlesungen über Geschichte der Mathematik* (Leipzig, 1900–08, 4 vols.).

Vol. 1, from the beginnings to 1200 A.D. First published in 1880, 2d ed., 1894, 3d ed., 1907.

Vol. 2, from 1200 to 1668. First edition, 1892, 2d ed., 1900 (reprinted in 1913 without change).

Vol. 3, from 1668 to 1758. First edition, 1898; 2d ed., with only a few corrections and additions, 1901.

Vol. 4, from 1759 to 1799. Published in 1908, by a group of specialists under Cantor's direction, his own contribution being restricted to a brief conclusion.

These volumes at the time of their publication were almost as good as any history can ever hope to be. To be sure, there were many mistakes concerning details, some of which were gradually corrected by Gustaf Eneström (1852–1923)[1] and his collaborators in *Bibliotheca Mathematica*, but the general lines were remarkably sound. Since that time much progress has been made, especially with regard to the ancient and mediaeval period and oriental mathematics in general, and Cantor has now become very insufficient in those respects. If these defects were less fundamental, they might be corrected in a new edition; as it is, at least the history of ancient and mediaeval times must be entirely rewritten.

The French historian Paul Tannery (1843–1904) wrote various books and memoirs dealing with the history of mathematics, chiefly that of Greece and that of the seventeenth century. *La géometrie grecque, comment son histoire nous est parvenue et ce que nous en savons* (Paris, 1887). *Pour l'histoire de la science hellène: De Thalès à Empédocle* (Paris, 1887, 2d ed., 1930); cf. *Isis*, vol. 15, pp. 179–

---

[1] Wilhelm Lorey, "Gustav Eneström," *Isis*, vol. 8, pp. 313–320, with portrait (1926).

180. *Mémoires scientifiques*, edited by his widow since 1912; thus far (1936), 13 vols. published (see *Isis, passim*). It was necessary to mention Tannery in a general way, though there is no danger of his being overlooked, as his papers, all anterior to 1905, are often referred to by Cantor, Heath, Sarton, and others.

I shall quote now a series of books completing Cantor's monumental history, and constituting with it a primary shelf of reference.

Otto Neugebauer, *Vorlesungen über Geschichte der antiken mathematischen Wissenschaften*, vol. 1. Vorgriechische Mathematik (Berlin, 1934); cf. *Isis*, vol. 24, pp. 151–153.

The main texts of Egyptian mathematics have been edited as follows:

The Rhind Mathematical Papyrus, ed. by Arnold Buffum Chace, Ludlow Bull, Henry Parker Manning and Raymond Clare Archibald, Oberlin, Ohio (2 vols., 1927–29); cf. *Isis*, vol. 14, pp. 251–255. Includes an elaborate bibliography of Egyptian (and Babylonian) mathematics by Archibald.

Mathematischer Papyrus des staatlichen Museums der schönen Künste in Moskau, ed. by W. W. Struve and B. A. Turajeff (Berlin, 1930); cf. *Isis*, vol. 16, pp. 148–155.

The texts of Mesopotamian mathematics have just been printed in

Mathematische Keilschrifttexte, ed. by O. Neugebauer (Berlin, 1935, 2 vols.). Including a bibliography of Babylonian mathematics.

The standard work for the history of Greek mathematics is

Sir Thomas Heath, *A History of Greek Mathematics* (Oxford, 1921, 2 vols.); cf. *Isis*, vol. 4, pp. 532–535. There is an abbreviated edition in a single volume, *A Manual of Greek Mathematics* (Oxford, 1931); cf. *Isis*, vol. 16, pp. 450–451.

Gino Loria, *Le scienze esatte nell' antica Grecia* (2d ed., Milano, 1914); cf. *Isis*, vol. 1, pp. 714–716. Covers a wider field than Heath, and is less elaborate, yet very valuable.

For Hindu mathematics, see

George Rusby Kaye (1866–1929), "Indian Mathematics," in *Isis*, vol. 2, pp. 326–356 (1919).

Sâradâkânta Gânguli, "Notes on Indian Mathematics: A Criticism of George Rusby Kaye's Interpretation," in *Isis*, vol. 12, pp. 132–145 (1929).

Bibhutibhusan Datta, *The Science of the Śulba: A Study in Early Hindu Geometry* (Calcutta, 1932); cf. *Isis*, vol. 22, pp. 272–277.

Bibhutibhusan Datta and Avadhesh Narayan Singh, *History of Hindu Mathematics: A Source Book*. Part 1, Numeral Notations and Arithmetic (Lahore, 1935: 282 pp.).

For mathematics in Eastern Asia, see

Yoshio Mikami, *The Development of Mathematics in China and Japan* (Leipzig, 1913).

David Eugene Smith and Yoshio Mikami, *A History of Japanese Mathematics* (Chicago, 1914); cf. *Isis*, vol. 2, pp. 410–413.

For general reference, especially with regard to mediaeval and oriental mathematics:

George Sarton, *Introduction to the History of Science* (2 vols. in 3, Washington, 1927–31). Vol. 1, From Homer to Omar Khayyam, 1927; vol. 2, From Rabbi ben Ezra to Roger Bacon, 1931; vol. 3, Fourteenth Century, in preparation.

Errata and addenda to these volumes are published periodically in the critical bibliographies of *Isis*, beginning with the nineteenth in vol. 8 for the first volume, and with the thirty-first in vol. 16 for the second.

II. HANDBOOKS

There are a number of small treatises on the history of mathematics, most of which are sufficient. The average level is far superior to that of books on the history of science. Indeed, some of these books, like Smith's and Cajori's, contain valuable materials not available elsewhere. I can mention only a few of these treatises.

Hieronymus Georg Zeuthen (1839–1920), *Geschichte der Mathematik im Altertum und Mittelalter* (Copenhagen, 1896). French translation by Jean Mascart, revised by the author (Paris, 1902). *Geschichte der Mathematik im XVI. und XVII. Jahrhundert* (Leipzig, 1903).

Zeuthen's books are important because of his mathematical interpretations; he was himself a creative mathematician and had a keener sense of mathematical subtleties than Cantor.

Walter William Rouse Ball (1850–1925), *A Short Account of the History of Mathematics* (London, 1888; sixth edition, 1915); cf. *Isis*, vol. 1, p. 561. This history has enjoyed more popularity than any other; though obsolescent, it may still prove of use. See Florian Cajori, "W. W. R. Ball," in *Isis*, vol. 8, pp. 321–324, portrait (1926).

Siegmund Günther (1848–1923), *Geschichte der Mathematik*. I. Teil, Bis Cartesius (Leipzig, 1908).

Heinrich Wieleitner (1874–1931), *Geschichte der Mathematik*. II. Teil, Von Cartesius bis zur Wende des 18. Jahrhunderts (Leipzig, 1911–21, 2 parts). See Julius Ruska, "Heinrich Wieleitner," in *Isis*, vol. 18, pp. 150–165, portrait (1932).

Florian Cajori (1859–1930), *A History of Mathematics* (New York, 1895; revised and enlarged edition, 1919). See R. C. Archibald, "Florian Cajori," in *Isis*, vol. 17, pp. 384–407, portrait (1932).

Cajori is especially valuable for the modern period. He deals, very briefly it is true, with a large number of mathematicians of the nineteenth and twentieth centuries.

David Eugene Smith, *History of Mathematics* (Boston, 1923–25, 2 vols.); cf. *Isis*, vol. 6, pp. 440–444; vol. 8, pp. 221–225. This is restricted to elementary mathematics, but contains an abundance of new and out of the way information, and many illustrations. Smith's books constitute the best introduction to the subject.

Gino Loria, *Storia delle matematiche* (Torino, 1929–33, 3 vols.). Vol. 1, to the Renaissance, 1929; vol. 2, sixteenth and seventeenth centuries, 1931; vol. 3, eighteenth and nineteenth centuries, 1933; cf. *Isis*, vol. 13, p. 228; vol. 19, p. 231; vol. 22, p. 598. Includes a good general account of modern mathematics.

To these handbooks may be added two so-called source-books. Heinrich Wieleitner, *Mathematische Quellenbücher* (Berlin, 1927–29, 4 small vols.). These volumes, containing a series of annotated extracts from mathematical classics, deal respectively with (1) arithmetic and algebra, (2) geometry and trigonometry, (3) analytical and synthetic geometry, (4) infinitesimal calculus. Cf. *Isis*, vol. 11, p. 240; vol. 12, p. 413.

David Eugene Smith, *A Source Book in Mathematics* (New York, 1929); cf. *Isis*, vol. 14, pp. 268–270. Arranged in topical order: number, algebra, geometry, probability, calculus. Unfortunately the selection begins only with the end of the fifteenth century; this is not the author's fault, but is due to the stupid programme of the collection in which it is included. On that account, if on no other, Wieleitner's source-book is preferable.

III. Treatises Devoted to the History of Special Branches of Mathematics

Before dealing with the special branches two more general books must be mentioned.

Johannes Tropfke, *Geschichte der Elementar-Mathematik* (first ed., Leipzig. 1902–03, 2 vols.). This first edition is cited only for the sake of curiosity. Soon after its publication the author began the preparation of a second edition, which was published in seven volumes from 1921 to 1924. The publication of a third edition began in 1930. I indicate the contents of each volume, with the dates of the second and (so far as it is published) third editions of each.

Vol. 1, computation, 1921, 1930. Vol. 2, general arithmetic, 1921, 1933. Vol. 3, proportions, equations, 1922. Vol. 4, plane geometry, 1923. Vol. 5, trigonometry, 1923. Vol. 6, analysis (i.e., series, computation of interest, combinations, probabilities, continued fractions, maxima and minima), analytical geometry, 1924. Vol. 7, stereometry, indices, 1924. See *Isis*, vol. 5, pp. 182–186, and *passim*.

The third edition is completely ready in manuscript, but its publication has been temporarily discontinued because of Germany's economic difficulties. This is very unfortunate, for Tropfke's history is a mine of information on every branch of elementary mathematics, and the historian must always consult it.

Florian Cajori (1859–1930), *A History of Mathematical Notations* (Chicago, 1928–29, 2 vols.); cf. *Isis*, vol. 12, pp. 332–336; vol. 13, pp. 129–130.

Arithmetic. David Eugene Smith, *Rara Arithmetica* (Boston, 1908). D. E. Smith and L. C. Karpinski, *The Hindu-Arabic Numerals* (Boston, 1911). Louis Charles Karpinski, *The History of Arithmetic* (Chicago, 1925); cf. *Isis*, vol. 8, pp. 231–232. Tobias Dantzig, *Number, the Language of Science* (New York, 1930; cf.

Isis, vol. 16, pp. 455–459; 2d ed., 1933; cf. *Isis*, vol. 20, p. 592).

Richard Brown, *A History of Accounting and Accountants* (Edinburgh, 1905).

Theory of Numbers. Leonard Eugene Dickson, *History of the Theory of Numbers* (Washington, 1919–23, 3 vols.).

Vol. 1, divisibility and primality, 1919; cf. *Isis*, vol. 3, pp. 446–448. Vol. 2, Diophantine analysis, 1920; cf. *Isis*, vol. 4, pp. 107–108. Vol. 3, quadratic and higher forms, 1923; cf. *Isis*, vol. 6, pp. 96–98.

These volumes do not contain a history in the usual sense of the word, but very elaborate collections of facts with the dates and references relative to each. The work is a magnificent introduction to the history of the subject.

Algebra. Pietro Cossali (1748–1815), *Origine, trasporto in Italia, primi progressi in essa dell' algebra. Storia critica di nuove disquisizioni analitiche o metafisiche arrichita* (Parma, 1797–99, 2 vols.).

Pietro Franchini (1768–1837), *La storia dell' algebra e de' suoi principali scrittori sino al secolo XIX rettificata, illustrata ed estesa col mezzo degli originali documenti* (Lucca, 1827).

Though obsolete in many respects, those two volumes must still be consulted.

H. G. Zeuthen, Sur l'origine de l'algèbre (Danske Videnskabernes Selskab, *Mathematisk-Fysiske Meddelelser*, ii, 4) (Copenhagen, 1919, 70 pp.).

Determinants. Sir Thomas Muir (1844–1934), *The Theory of Determinants in the Historical Order of Development* (London, 1906–23, 4 vols.), with supplement, *Contributions to the History of Determinants, 1900–1920* (London, 1930).

The same remark applies to these books as to Dickson's above (cf. *Isis*, vol. 4, p. 199; vol. 7, p. 312; vol. 16, p. 510). Muir's work is really an analytic catalogue of all papers dealing with determinants, but he has often overlooked very important matters because these were included in papers specifically devoted to other subjects. This illustrates a fundamental weakness of such undertakings.

Trigonometry. Anton von Braunmühl (1853–1908), *Vorlesungen über Geschichte der Trigonometrie* (Leipzig, 1900–03, 2 vols.).

Geometry. Michel Chasles (1793–1880), *Aperçu historique sur l'origine et le développement des méthodes en géométrie* (Bruxelles, 1837;

2d ed., Paris, 1875). The same, *Rapport sur les progrès de la géométrie* (Paris, 1870: 388 pp.).

Gino Loria, *Il passato e il presente delle principali teorie geometriche* (Torino, 1887; 2d ed., 1897; 3d, 1907; 4th, 1931); cf. *Isis*, vol. 19, pp. 229–231.

Max Simon, *Über die Entwicklung der Elementar-Geometrie im XIX. Jahrhundert* (Leipzig, 1906: 286 pp.).

Analytical Geometry. Gino Loria, *Da Descartes e Fermat a Monge e Lagrange: Contributo alla storia della geometria analitica* (Roma, 1924); cf. *Isis*, vol. 8, p. 606.

Gino Loria, *Curve piane speciali algebriche e trascendenti* (Milano, 1930, 2 vols.); cf. *Isis*, vol. 14, p. 542; vol. 15, p. 467. Previously published in German (Leipzig, 1910–11, 2 vols.). Contains considerable historical information relative to each curve.

Descriptive Geometry. Noël Germinal Poudra (1794–1894), *Histoire de la perspective ancienne et moderne* (Paris, 1864).

Gino Loria, *Storia della geometria descrittiva dalle origini sino ai giorni nostri* (Milano, 1921); cf. *Isis*, vol. 5, pp. 181–182.

Synthetic Geometry. Ernst Kötter, "Die Entwickelung der synthetischen Geometrie, I. Theil: Von Monge bis auf Staudt, 1847," in the *Jahresbericht* of the Deutsche Mathematiker-Vereinigung, vol. 5, pt. 2 (Leipzig, 1898–1901: 514 pages). No more published.

Non-Euclidean Geometry. Friedrich Engel and Paul Stäckel, *Die Theorie der Parallellinien von Euklid bis auf Gauss, eine Urkundensammlung zur Vorgeschichte der nichteuklidischen Geometrie* (Leipzig, 1895: 336 pp.); and *Urkunden zur Geschichte der nichteuklidischen Geometrie*, vol. 1 in 2 parts, dealing with Lobachevskii (Leipzig, 1898–99); vol. 2 in 2 parts, dealing with Bólyai (1913).

Roberto Bonola (1874–1911), "Index Operum ad Geometriam Absolutam spectantium," pp. 81–154 in the memorial volume published by the Hungarian University of Kolozsvár for Bólyai's centenary in 1902. Also *La geometria non-euclidea: Esposizione storico-critica del suo sviluppo* (Bologna, 1906: 220 pages). German translation by Heinrich Liebmann (Leipzig, 1908: 252 pp., 76 fig.; 2d ed., 1919, reprinted in 1921). English translation by H. S. Carslaw (Chicago, 1921: 280 pp.).

Duncan M. Y. Sommerville, *Bibliography of Non-Euclidean Geometry, including the Theory of Parallels, the Foundation of Geometry, and*

Space of n *Dimensions* (London, 1911: 415 pp.). In chronological order, with subject and author indices.

Analysis. The early history of the differential and integral calculus (down to 1800) is naturally dealt with in vols. 3 and 4 of Cantor's *Vorlesungen*, but there is no history of modern analysis.

There is an outline of the history of functions of complex variables in Felice Casorati (1835–90), *Teorica delle funzioni di variabili complesse* (vol. 1, Pavia, 1868; no more published). The history down to 1865 covers 143 pages.

Calculus of Variations. Isaac Todhunter (1820–84), *History of the Calculus of Variations during the Nineteenth Century* (Cambridge, 1861: 544 pp.).

Theory of Probabilities. Isaac Todhunter, *History of the Mathematical Theory of Probability from the Time of Pascal to that of Laplace* (Cambridge, 1865: 640 pp.).

Helen M. Walker, *Studies in the History of Statistical Methods* (Baltimore, 1929: 237 pp., 12 ills.); cf. *Isis*, vol. 13, pp. 382–383.

IV. MATHEMATICS IN THE NINETEENTH AND TWENTIETH CENTURIES

Many of the books named in Section III deal with the modern history of mathematics, sometimes almost or quite exclusively. For example, in Muir's elaborate history of determinants we find mention of only eleven papers anterior to 1800: there were no others.

The best general view of nineteenth-century mathematics is the one contained in Cajori's *History of Mathematics* (2d ed., 1919). Almost half of the volume (pp. 278–516) is devoted to the nineteenth century and after. While it is only a bird's eye view, it is the most complete I know of. The information given is often so brief as to be unintelligible except to one well acquainted with the subject. However, it indicates the mutual relationship of many hundreds of mathematicians. It is a modest but excellent reference book.

The third volume of Loria's *Storia* (1933) contains also a good account, dealing with fewer mathematicians, but giving more space to each.

The most ambitious attempt to outline the history of modern mathematics was made by Felix Klein (1849–1925) in the form of lectures given in his own home during the war years. Klein was eminently qualified for this task, because he combined historical learning with mathematical depth to an unusual degree. These lectures were unfortunately interrupted by illness in 1919. They have been posthumously published; as far as they go they are very precious.

Felix Klein, *Vorlesungen über die Entwicklung der Mathematik im 19. Jahrhundert*. Part 1 edited by R. Courant and O. Neugebauer (Berlin, 1926: 400 pp.); cf. *Isis*, vol. 9, pp. 447–449. Part 2 edited by R. Courant and Stephan Cohn-Vossen (Berlin, 1927: 208 pp.); cf. *Isis*, vol. 10, p. 505.

These two volumes are so important that it is worth while to indicate their contents with some detail. I give for each chapter not only the title but the names of the principal mathematicians dealt with.

Part 1. Chapter 1. Gauss. 2. France and the École Polytechnique at the beginning of the century (Poisson, Fourier, Cauchy, Sadi Carnot, Poncelet, Coriolis, Monge, Galois). 3. Foundation of Crelle's *Journal* and blossoming of the German school (Crelle, Dirichlet, Abel, Jacobi, Moebius, Plücker, Steiner). 4. Development of algebraical geometry. Projective geometry (Staudt, Chasles, Cayley). Theory of invariants (Jacobi, Hesse, Cayley, Sylvester, Salmon). *n*-dimensional space and generalized complex numbers (Plücker, Riemann, Grassmann, Hamilton). 5. Mechanics and mathematical physics in Germany and England to c. 1880 (Hamilton, Jacobi, Routh. Neumann, Kirchhoff, Helmholtz, Green, MacCullagh, Stokes, W. Thomson, Maxwell). 6. General theory of functions of complex variables (Riemann, Weierstrass). 7. Deeper study of the essence of algebraical forms (Clebsch, Abel, Gordan, Brill, Noether. Kummer, Kronecker, Dedekind, Weber, Weierstrass, Hurwitz, Hilbert, Minkowski). 8. Theories of groups and functions, especially automorphic functions (from Lagrange to Galois and C. Jordan, Gauss, Riemann, Picard. Abel, Jacobi, Hermite. Poincaré).

Part 2 is only a fragment of a little more than two hundred pages. It contains three chapters dealing with what might be called the preparation of the general theory of relativity, representing the substance of lectures given in 1915–17. Klein had put together materials for many chapters, of which only these three were sufficiently advanced to be edited. 1. Principles of the linear theory of invariants. 2. Special theory of relativity in mechanics and mathematical physics. 3. Groups of analytic point transformations on the basis of a quadratic differential form. The fourth chapter would have been devoted to the general theory of relativity and Hamiltonian mechanics, but it was too inchoate to be edited.

Pierre Sergescu, *Les sciences mathématiques* (Paris, 1933: 168 pp.); cf. *Isis*, vol. 23, p. 539. This is a part of the *Tableau du XXe siècle* (1900–33), a title here doubly misleading because Sergescu's account is not restricted to the twentieth century but is restricted to France. It is an interesting cross-section of the development of modern mathematics.

Another valuable approach is given by the history of schools, societies, and journals. With regard to schools the most obvious examples are the École Normale Supérieure and the École Polytechnique, both of which were founded in Paris at the end of the eighteenth century and played an important part in the development of modern mathematics.

École Polytechnique. *Livre du centenaire, 1794–1894* (Paris, 1894–97, 3 vols., many portraits). Vol. 1 deals with science (1895: 618 pp.).

Le centenaire de l'École Normale, 1795–1895 (Paris, 1895: 746 pp., many portraits).

In general, whenever the mathematical topic whose history one is investigating was studied with particular success in a certain university, it is worth while to consult the histories or commemorative publications of that university. In many cases universities have devoted special publications to their mathematical schools.

With regard to journals, it is well to consult their commemorative volumes and indices. The most interesting table for the historian is:

Acta Mathematica, 1882–1912: Table générale des tomes 1–35, rédigée par Marcel Riesz (Uppsala, 1913: 180 pp.). Including short biographies and portraits of all the contributors, it constitutes the best iconographic survey of *homo geometricus*.

However, the best approach to the history of modern mathematics is the study of the biographies of the great leaders. Students should read a few of these, or at least one, and after that they should read a few original memoirs. Such an introduction to the history of mathematics, in spite of its casualness, or perhaps because of it, is excellent, for it satisfies at one and the same time the logical needs of the historian and his desires as scientist and humanist.

I shall note first a few collections of mathematical biographies. The histories of schools, academies, societies, journals, often include such collections. For example, see the *Livre du centenaire* of the École Polytechnique, mentioned above.

Alexander Macfarlane, *Lectures on Ten British Mathematicians of the Nineteenth Century* (New York, 1916: 148 pp.). The ten are George Peacock, Augustus De Morgan, Sir W. R. Hamilton, George Boole, Arthur Cayley, W. K. Clifford, H. J. S. Smith, J. J. Sylvester, T. P. Kirkman, Isaac Todhunter.

Alexander Macfarlane, *Lectures on Ten British Physicists of the Nineteenth Century* (New York, 1919: 144 pp.). These physicists were also in different degrees mathematicians: J. C. Maxwell, W. J. M. Rankine, P. G. Tait, Kelvin, Charles Babbage, William Whewell, Sir G. G. Stokes, Sir G. B. Airy, J. C. Adams, Sir J. F. W. Herschel. Cf. *Isis*, vol. 3, p. 291.

Ganesh Prasad (1876–1935), *Some Great Mathematicians of the Nineteenth Century: Their Lives and their Works* (Benares, 1933–34. 2 vols.). Cf. *Isis*, vol. 22, pp. 359, 575.

Vol. 1: Gauss, Cauchy, Abel, Jacobi, Weierstrass, Riemann. Vol. 2: Cayley, Hermite, Kronecker, Brioschi, Cremona, Darboux, G. Cantor, Mittag-Leffler, Klein, Poincaré. A third volume was contemplated, but its appearance has been rendered uncertain by the author's untimely death. I do not know whether vol. 3 was ready for publication, or sufficiently advanced to be completed by an editor.[1]

Biographies of mathematicians are included in the publications of the innumerable societies and academies. Some of these biographies are perfunctory or frigidly academic, others are very valuable. The biographies written by the Secrétaires perpétuels for mathematics of the Académie des Sciences are often very

[1] See Archibald in *Scripta Mathematica*, vol. 3, p. 274 (1935).

good; they are published in the *Mémoires de l'Académie* and many are also available in separate volumes; this is the case for the biographies written by François Arago (*Oeuvres*, vols. 1–3, 1854–55; some of these were translated into English by W. H. Smyth, Baden Powell, and Robert Grant, as *Biographies of Distinguished Scientific Men* (London, 1857)), Joseph Bertrand (*Éloges académiques*, 1890; nouvelle série, 1902), Gaston Darboux (*Éloges académiques et discours*, 1912), Émile Picard (*Discours et mélanges*, 1922, *Mélanges de mathématiques et de physique*, 1924, *Éloges et discours*, 1931). See also Henri Poincaré, *Savants et écrivains* (1910), and Maurice d'Ocagne, *Hommes et choses de science* (3 vols., 1930, 1932, 1936).

For individual biographies see Appendix below.

V. PHILOSOPHY AND METHODOLOGY

It is more difficult to make a selection of books on the philosophy of mathematics than on the history of it, because philosophical qualities and defects are not so tangible as historical ones, because the best philosophical books for one person are not necessarily the best for another, and, finally, because my own experience is poorer in this field. I will name a few books which are valuable in different ways, and among which almost any student ought to be able to find what he needs; I do not say that other books of which I do not know are not valuable.

Jean Marie Constant Duhamel (1797–1872), *Des méthodes dans les sciences de raisonnement* (Paris, 1865–73, 5 vols.). 1, Des méthodes communes à toutes les sciences de raisonnement (1865: 104 pp.); 2, Application des méthodes générales à la science des nombres et à la science de l'étendue (1866: 464 pp.); 3, Application de la science des nombres à la science de l'étendue (1868: 457 pp.); 4, Application des méthodes générales à la science des forces (1870: 486 pp.); 5, Essai d'une application des méthodes à la science de l'homme moral (1873: 102 pp.).

Though partly obsolete, this work is still valuable, and it is historically important, being the first large undertaking of its kind.

After Duhamel, who is named first for chronological reasons, I must give the pride of place to Henri Poincaré's three famous volumes, *La science et l'hypothèse* (1908), *La valeur de la science* (1909),

Science et méthode (1909), translated into many languages. The English translation by George Bruce Halsted is available in a single volume (New York, 1913; many times reprinted).

After Poincaré's book I should mention Bertrand Russell (now third Earl Russell), *Principles of Mathematics*, vol. 1 (Cambridge, 1903: 564 pp.). This was not continued, at least in that form, but it gave occasion to another and greater work.

Alfred North Whitehead and Bertrand Russell, *Principia Mathematica* (Cambridge, 1910–13, 3 vols.; 2d ed., 1925–27); cf. *Isis*, vol. 8, pp. 226–231; vol. 10, pp. 513–519. The *Principia* is not a book to 'read'; it is as severely technical as any book can be, and its study requires a hard initiation. Historians whose purpose is simply to understand the meaning and drift of mathematics will do better to leave it alone.

Russell's pregnant volume of 1903 gave birth also to

Louis Couturat, *Les principes des mathématiques, avec un appendice sur la philosophie des mathématiques de Kant* (Paris, 1905: 320 pp.).

The following books are named in the chronological order of their first editions.

Aurel Voss, *Über des Wesen der Mathematik* (Leipzig, 1908, 98 pp.; 2d ed., 1913).

Alfred North Whitehead, *An Introduction to Mathematics* (London, 1911, 256 pp.; in the *Home University Library*). Very elementary but very wise.

Léon Brunschvicg, *Les étapes de la philosophie mathématique* (Paris, 1912: 602 pp.); cf. *Isis*, vol. 1, pp. 577–589, 721–734. Written by a philosopher for philosophers; too prolix and too remote from the applications for the mathematician.

Philip E. B. Jourdain (1879–1919), *The Nature of Mathematics* (London, 1913, 92 pp.; in *The People's Books*); cf. *Isis*, vol. 1, p. 562. Brief but substantial. Price, 6d. There is a biography of the author by his wife in *Isis*, vol. 5, pp. 129–133, portrait (1923).

Bertrand Russell, *Introduction to Mathematical Philosophy* (London, 1919, 208 pp.; 2d ed., 1920, reprinted, 1924). Written for mathematical students who are not acquainted with logical symbolism and thus are unable to read the *Principia*.

Pierre Boutroux (1880–1922), *Les principes de l'analyse mathématique: Exposé historique et critique* (1914–19, 2 vols.); cf. *Isis*, vol. 1, pp. 577–589, 734–742; vol. 4, pp. 96–107.

Pierre Boutroux, *L'idéal scientifique des mathématiciens* (Paris, 1920: 274 pp.); cf. *Isis*, vol. 4, pp. 93–96. German translation (Leipzig, 1927).

Boutroux's books constitute a magnificent introduction to mathematics for the historian as well as for the philosopher. The larger treatise in two volumes is especially to be recommended to those who are not professional mathematicians because of its concreteness. An English version of the smaller book has long been overdue.

Federigo Enriques, *Per la storia della logica: I principii e l'ordine della scienza nel concetto dei pensatori matematici* (Bologna, 1922: 302 pp.); cf. *Isis*, vol. 5, p. 469. French translation in 1926, German translation in 1927, English translation by Jerome Rosenthal, *The Historic Development of Logic* (New York, 1929). This book fully deserved its international success, for it is brief, clear, and instructive, perhaps the best guide for the history of the logic of science.

Hermann Weyl, *The Open World* (New Haven, 1932; 90 pp.). The same, *Mind and Nature* (Philadelphia, 1934: 106 pp.); cf. *Isis*, vol. 23, pp. 281–284.

Gino Loria, *Metodi matematici: Essenza, tecnica, applicazioni* (Milano, Hoepli, 1935: 291 pp.); cf. *Isis*, vol. 25, p. 278.

VI. BIBLIOGRAPHY

A. *Guides*

Ernst Wölffing, *Mathematischer Bücherschatz. I. Teil: Reine Mathematik* (Leipzig, 1903, 452 pp.: *Abhandlungen zur Geschichte der mathematischen Wissenschaften*, Heft 16, 1). This is a list of mathematical titles classified under 313 headings, such as 1, history of mathematics, 2, philosophy of mathematics, 3, symbols, 4, mathematical logic, . . . 113, functions of complex variables, special, . . . 308, involution, . . . 312, collections of formulas, 313, games. The items of each section are put in alphabetical order, without selection or criticism.

Felix Müller (1843–   ), *Führer durch die mathematische Literatur, mit besonderer Berücksichtigung der historisch wichtigen Schriften* (Leipzig, 1909, 262 pp.; *Abhandlungen zur Geschichte der mathematischen*

Wissenschaften, Heft 27). A much better book than the preceding; it contains fewer titles, but it is more critical.

Gino Loria, *Guida allo studio della storia delle matematiche* (Milano, 1916, 244 pp.: in the *Manuali Hoepli*). More limited in scope than Müller's book, for it concerns the needs of the historian of mathematics rather than the mathematician in general, but very good.

George Abram Miller, *Historical Introduction to Mathematical Literature* (New York, 1916: 315 pp.). Contains information of the same kind as that provided by Müller and Loria, but mixed with information of the kind given in histories of mathematics. Hence as a history it is inferior to pure histories, and as a guide it is inferior to Müller and Loria.

The best two of these four books are those of Müller and Loria, but, as in the case of any other tool, their usefulness depends on their owner's familiarity with them. Students should examine these books carefully in order that they may know what to find in them and how to find it.

B. *Encyclopaedias*

Historians of mathematics will find an abundance of information, historical as well as topical, in the great encyclopaedia promoted by the scientific academies of Göttingen, Leipzig, Munich, and Vienna, and later by the academies of Berlin and Heidelberg as well:

Encyklopädie der mathematischen Wissenschaften mit Einschluss ihrer Anwendungen (Leipzig, Teubner, 1898–1935).

This great work has just been completed, its publication having been stretched over nearly forty years. It is divided into six main parts, each of which includes a number of thick volumes.

I. Arithmetic and Algebra. In 2 parts, edited by Wilhelm Franz Meyer (1898–1904).

II. Analysis. 3 parts in 5 volumes. Edited by Heinrich Burkhardt, Wilhelm Wirtinger, Robert Fricke, and Emil Hilb (1899–1927).

III. Geometry. 3 parts in 6 volumes. Edited by W. F. Meyer and Hans Mohrmann (1907–34).

IV. Mechanics. 4 parts in 4 volumes, and an index volume. Edited by Felix Klein and Conrad H. Müller (1896–1935). The index volume, the last fascicle of the whole work, includes an epilogue by Constantin Carathéodory (1935).

V. Physics. 3 parts in 3 volumes. Edited by Arnold Sommer-feld (1903–26).

VI, 1. Geodesy and Geophysics. Edited by Philipp Furt-wängler and Emil Wiechert (1906–25).

VI, 2. Astronomy. In 2 volumes. Edited by Karl Schwarz-schild, Samuel Oppenheim, and Walther von Dyck (1905–34).

It was planned to publish a new edition of the encyclopaedia in French, the first part of which appeared in 1904. The *Ency-clopédie des sciences mathématiques pures et appliquées*, under the general editorship of Jules Molk (1857–1914), was not simply a transla-tion of the German work, but a revision (with attention to the historical point of view)[1] and an extension of it. Some 32 parts were actually published, being fragments of 27 volumes, none of which was completed. Then the undertaking was abandoned (1915). Neither the war nor the editor's death can justify such a betrayal of the unfortunate subscribers. It should be noted that the catastrophe is even greater than it may seem at first. As it is hardly possible to remember which parts of each volume are available and which are not, one altogether loses the habit of consulting them, and the parts which have been published are almost as if they had never been.

C. *Large Catalogues*

Johann Christian Poggendorff (1796–1877), *Biographisch-literarisches Handwörterbuch zur Geschichte der exakten Wissenschaften* (Leipzig, 1863, 2 vols.). Vol. 3 for the period 1858–83 (1898). Vol. 4 for the period 1883–1904 (1904). Vol. 5 for the period 1904–22 (1926).

Royal Society of London, *Catalogue of Scientific Papers, 1800–1900* (1867–1925, 19 vols.). Subject index (only 4 vols. published, 1908–14).

International Catalogue of Scientific Literature (1901–15).

[1] G. Eneström, "Jules Molk als Förderer der exakten mathematisch-historischen Forschung," in *Bibliotheca Mathematica*, 3d series, vol. 14, pp. 336–340, with portrait (1915).

These two gigantic publications have been described in my *Study of the History of Science.* I shall consider here only their mathematical parts.

The subject index of the Royal Society *Catalogue* is incomplete, but the mathematical volume is available, as well as two other volumes of special interest to mathematicians, "Mechanics" and "Physics." "Astronomy," however, has not been published.

Vol. 1, Pure Mathematics (Cambridge, 1908: 724 pp.), contains 38,748 entries. The classification is decimal, the numbers 00xy referring to philosophy, history, biography, and other general topics.

Turning to the *International Catalogue*, fourteen volumes of section A, Mathematics, have appeared, dealing with the literature of 1901–15, classified exactly as in the Royal Society subject index.

These two catalogues — Royal Society and International — thus enable the historian to examine very conveniently the immense mathematical literature of the period 1800–1915.

D. *Journals*

A very large proportion of the mathematical literature is published in journals. This is especially true for modern mathematics, or even for the period posterior to 1665, when the two earliest journals containing mathematical articles began to appear, the *Philosophical Transactions* and the *Journal des savants.*[1] Down to 1700 there were only 17 journals containing mathematical articles; 54 were added in the first half of the eighteenth century; 156 in the second half of the same century; there were some 950 such journals in the nineteenth century.[2] Seven hundred serials are referred to in the first volume of the subject index to the Royal Society *Catalogue.*

On account of the abundance of that literature and its wide dispersion, special journals have been established the purpose of which is primarily bibliographical. The three most important of these are the *Bulletin des sciences mathématiques*, first edited by

[1] Petre Sergescu, "Les mathématiques dans le Journal des savants," in *Osiris*, vol. 1, pp. 568–583 (1936).

[2] Figures given by Felix Müller in *Jahresbericht der Deutschen Mathematiker Vereinigung*, vol. 12, p. 439 (1903).

Gaston Darboux, now by Émile Picard (vol. 1, 1870; vol. 70 in 1935; from 1870 to 1884 the title was *Bulletin des sciences mathématiques et astronomiques*), the *Jahrbuch über die Fortschritte der Mathematik* (vol. 1, for the year 1868, published in 1871; vol. 61 in 1935), and the *Revue semestrielle des publications mathématiques*, published under the auspices of the Mathematical Society of Amsterdam and since 1932 under the combined auspices of the Prussian Academy and that society (vol. 1 in 1893; vol. 40 in 1935).

Felix Müller, "Abgekürzte Titel von Zeitschriften mathematischen Inhalts," and "Erläuterungen und historische Notizen zu vorstehendem Verzeichnisse," in *Jahresbericht der Deutschen Mathematiker-Vereinigung*, vol. 12, pp. 427–444 (1903).

H. S. White, "Forty Years' Fluctuations in Mathematical Research," in Science, vol. 42, pp. 105–113 (1915).

The best key to these journals until 1915 is provided by the three catalogues mentioned above in Section C. In addition to these, some journals have published special indices of their own, which it is unnecessary to mention here.

VII. Journals on the History of Mathematics

Though it is out of the question to deal separately with all the journals which are wholly or partly mathematical, I must not fail to mention the journals devoted primarily to the history of mathematics.

The most important are, in chronological order:

1. 1868. *Bullettino di bibliografia e di storia delle scienze matematiche e fisiche*. Edited by Prince Baldassare Boncompagni (1821–94). Rome (1868–87, 20 large quartos). Indici dei venti tomi, in vol. 20, pp. 697–748 (1890).

This was a bibliographical journal as well as a purely historical one; the line is not always easy to draw. On the other hand Darboux's *Bulletin*, mentioned previously with other bibliographical journals, might have been mentioned here, for it contains many historical contributions. In any case, Boncompagni's *Bullettino* was the first organ of the history of mathematics. It is a splendid collection, wherein a large number of ancient mathematical documents were first published (see Indice di documenti inediti, vol. 20, pp. 729–748).

2. 1877. *Abhandlungen zur Geschichte der mathematischen Wissen-schaften mit Einschluss ihrer Anwendungen.* Edited by Moritz Cantor (Leipzig, 1877–1913, 30 parts).

Parts 1 to 10 were issued as supplements to the *Zeitschrift für Mathematik und Physik.*

3. 1884. *Bibliotheca Mathematica.* Edited by Gustav Eneström (1884–1915, 30 vols.).

First series, 3 vols., quarto, a total of 566 pp. (Stockholm, 1884–86). Begun as a kind of supplement to *Acta Mathematica*, it was published in the same format.

Second series, 13 vols., octavo (Stockholm, 1887–99).

Third series, 14 vols., octavo (Leipzig, 1900–15).

4. 1898. *Bollettino di bibliografia e storia delle scienze matematiche.* Edited by Gino Loria (Torino, 1898–1917, 21 vols.).

From 1919 this has been continued as an appendix to the *Bollettino di matematica* as the sezione storico-bibliografica per cura di Gino Loria. The purpose of Loria's journal, in both forms, is partly historical and partly bibliographical.

5. 1913. *Isis.* Quarterly organ of the History of Science Society and bibliographical organ of the International Academy of the History of Science. Edited by George Sarton (vol. 1, 1913–14; in 1936, vols. 24 to 26).

Contains a large number of papers on the history of mathematics. The critical bibliography is by far the most elaborate of its kind, but it is classified for the use of the historian of science rather than for the historian of mathematics. That is, it will not suffice to consult the section "Mathematics," which includes only a few of the mathematical notes. The main classification is chronological, and hence studies on al-Khwârizmî and on Gauss are classified in the sections dealing respectively with the first half of the ninth century and with the first half of the nineteenth. The second classification is historical, and hence studies on Talmudic or Chinese mathematics are classified, not under mathematics, but under Israel or China. The section "Mathematics" contains only the notes which could not be classified otherwise.

6. 1927. *Archiv für Geschichte der Mathematik, der Naturwissen-schaften, und der Technik.* Edited by Julius Schuster (Leipzig, 1927–30, vols. 10 to 13).

Continuation of the *Archiv für die Geschichte der Naturwissen-*

schaften und der Technik (Leipzig, 1909–22, 9 vols.; vol. 9, 1920–22, only 126 pp.).

7. 1929. *Quellen und Studien zur Geschichte der Mathematik, Astronomie, und Physik.* Edited by Otto Neugebauer, Julius Stenzel (1883–1935), and Otto Toeplitz (Berlin, 1929, etc.) and published in two sections:

A. Quellen (vol. 1, 1930; vol. 3, in two parts, in 1935).

B. Studien (vol. 1, 1929–31; vol. 3, in 1935).

8. 1932. *Scripta Mathematica.* Edited by Jekuthiel Ginsburg (vol. 1, New York, 1932–33; vol. 3 in 1935).

9. 1936. *Osiris.* Studies on the history and philosophy of science and on the history of learning and culture. Edited by George Sarton.

Vol. 1 (778 pp., 24 figs., 35 facs., 22 pls.) published in January, 1936, and dedicated to David Eugene Smith, is a collection of 38 papers on the history of mathematics.

More information on some of these journals and on other journals will be found in G. Sarton, "Soixante-deux revues et collections relatives à l'histoire des sciences," in *Isis*, vol. 2, pp. 132–161 (1914).

The nine journals above mentioned might be divided into three groups according to their bibliographical interests. I. Journals attempting to give a complete bibliography of the history of mathematics: nos. 1, 3, 5. II. Journals containing bibliographical information without system and without attempt at completeness: nos. 4, 6, 8. III. No bibliography of current publications: nos. 2, 7, 9.

For the making of any bibliography of the history of mathematics, it will generally suffice to consult nos. 1, 3, 5, that is, Boncompagni for the period 1868–87, Eneström for the period 1884–1915, Sarton for the period beginning in 1913 or a little before.

.

VIII. Centres of Research

A. *Academies of Science*

Every academy of science has a mathematical section or devotes some attention to mathematics in its publications or otherwise. Academies organize competitions and promote mathematical research in various ways. They have occasionally shown some interest in the history of mathematics.

B. *Mathematical Societies*

By the beginning of the nineteenth century science had already developed to such an extent that academies had become somewhat obsolete. They preserved some kind of administrative unity, but they lost their organic unity, as it became generally impossible for each member to be interested in the activities of the majority of the other members. Hence it was necessary to create new societies devoted to the promotion of special sciences. The mathematical societies were relatively slow in appearing.[1]

1865. London Mathematical Society.
1872. Société Mathématique de France.
1883. Edinburgh Mathematical Society.
1884. Circolo Matematico di Palermo.
1888. American Mathematical Society (first called New York M. S.).
1890. Deutsche Mathematiker Vereinigung.
1907. Indian Mathematical Society.
1911. Sociedad Matemática Española.
1915. Mathematical Association of America.

These societies, and other similar ones existing in many other countries, encourage the study and the teaching of mathematics, but they pay relatively little attention to its history.

C. *International Congresses*

In spite of the fact that many mathematical societies have an international membership, each of them is necessarily most concerned with the problems of mathematical study and teaching

---

[1] That is, influential societies, organized like academies and supporting special publications. Local groups of mathematicians were organized much earlier, and perhaps in more centres (e.g., universities) than we can realize. Two interesting examples are the Mathematische Gesellschaft zu Hamburg founded in 1690 (for which see the *Festschrift* it published two centuries later) and the Mathematical Society of Spitalfields (in London) founded in 1717 (*Nature*, vol. 64, p. 478, 1901).

within its national boundaries. By the end of the century this was felt to be insufficient, and efforts were made to supplement these national organizations by international ones. The first two international congresses were:

1. 1889. Paris. Congrès International de Bibliographie des Sciences Mathématiques.
2. 1893. Chicago. International Mathematical Congress.

However, these two congresses are not counted in the official list of international congresses.

1. 1897. Zurich.
2. 1900. Paris.
3. 1904. Heidelberg.
4. 1908. Rome.
5. 1912. Cambridge.

The sixth meeting, Stockholm, 1916, could not take place because of the War. After the War, a new series of congresses was begun, the internationality of which was at first incomplete.

1. 1920. Strasbourg.
2. 1924. Toronto.
3. 1928. Bologna.
4. 1932. Zurich.
5. 1936. Oslo.

The Oslo congress is thus the fifth congress of the new series, or the tenth or twelfth congress of the whole series.

Each of these congresses has devoted a part of its attention to the history and philosophy of mathematics, a special section being generally reserved for these two subjects. It may be worth while for the historian to examine the publications of these congresses with special reference to their historical and philosophical questions.

In addition, the literature of those congresses will be of great value to the later historian, because they will help him to determine the fluctuations of mathematical interests from year to year and the mathematical atmosphere of each definite period. Therefore the publications of the international congresses should be kept in good order in our historico-mathematical libraries.

Questions relative to the history and philosophy of mathematics have also been periodically discussed in other international congresses, to wit, the congresses of philosophy, of history, and those of the history of science and the philosophy of science, for all of which see my *Study of the History of Science*.

D. *Institutes and Libraries*

Every mathematical library is a natural centre for historical research as well as for mathematical research proper. For investigations on modern mathematics necessitate the availability of sets of mathematical periodicals, which are legion, or at least of sets of the most important ones, which are numerous enough. Such investigations can generally be conducted in every one of the largest libraries, and in the mathematical departments of the main universities.

One European library must be singled out, namely the one founded by the Swedish mathematician Gösta Mittag-Leffler and his wife in 1916 for the special benefit of mathematicians of the Scandinavian countries and Finland, but available also to those of other lands. It is located in Mittag-Leffler's old home in Midgård, Djursholm, near Stockholm. It was my privilege to visit this very rich library in the summer of 1934. The historical section is not very strong, but the archives contain a large number of letters of modern mathematicians. The publication of a calendar of these archives is very desirable.

Systematisk förteckning öfver G. Mittag-Lefflers Matematiska Bibliotek, upprättad af St. Grönfeldt, Stockholm-Djursholm (Uppsala, 1915: 706 coll.). *Institut mathématique des époux Mittag-Leffler* (Uppsala, 1916: 11 pp.).

Among American libraries, I will single out three. First, the David Eugene Smith Library bequeathed by D. E. Smith to Columbia University, and now an integral though distinct part of the Columbia Library. This is, I believe, the richest library on the history of mathematics available anywhere; it contains not only books and reprints, but abundant archives, portraits, medals, and instruments. See the description by Bertha M. Frick in *Osiris*, vol. 1, pp. 79–84 (1936).

The second is the library built up in Brown University by the late Chancellor Arnold Buffum Chace (1845–1932) and Raymond Clare Archibald. The third is the collection of early mathematical books gathered by George Arthur Plimpton in New York City.

Among Asiatic libraries, the best is perhaps that of the Hebrew University in Jerusalem, into which the very valuable collections [1] of the late Felix Klein are now incorporated.

[1] Books and periodicals, not reprints. To be more precise, there are two mathematical libraries in the Hebrew University, the Jewish National and University Library and the library of the Einstein Institute. Klein's library is in the Einstein Institute. Letter from Adolf Fraenkel, Jerusalem 3511.21.

APPENDIX

Biographies of Modern Mathematicians

As it is advisable for mathematicians who have historical tendencies to devote their attention chiefly to modern mathematics, I have compiled for their sake a list of some of the chief mathematicians of the nineteenth and twentieth centuries. I quote for each of them

(1) the best available biographies;
(2) editions of their collected works;
(3) editions of their correspondence.

These three items have been selected because they go together; in fact, they are sometimes parts of a single publication. The 'collected works' are often restricted to the papers and memoirs which were originally scattered in various periodicals or remained unpublished; they may or may not also include treatises originally published in book form. Thus the interest of 'collected works' varies very much in the case of different mathematicians, as some published their best writings in journals, while others gave the most convincing evidence of their genius in formal treatises.

Aside from the fact that any selection of mathematicians is subject to criticism (no two historians of mathematics would offer the same selections, though a good many names would probably be found in every list), my bibliography is *incomplete* and *superficial*. It is incomplete because I have mentioned only the publications known to me and easily available; it is superficial because my selection of biographies is not based upon a direct study of all of them, which would occupy a life-time.

In spite of these shortcomings (which may be gradually corrected)[1] I hope that my list, such as it is, will prove useful and stimulating.

Living mathematicians have not been included. I have omitted Lagrange and Monge, who died respectively in 1813 and 1818, because they are primarily eighteenth-century men,

[1] I shall be grateful to readers who are kind enough to send corrections, and these will be used as far as possible.

but I have included Lazare Carnot (d. 1823), Laplace (d. 1827), and Legendre (d. 1833), because some of their most important works belong to the nineteenth century.

The short indications sometimes added after a name, such as 'celestial mechanics,' 'theory of numbers,' are not meant as complete definitions of the man's activity, but simply as helps to the memory.

Additional information may be obtained from:

G. Eneström, "Bio-bibliographie der 1881–1900 verstorbenen Mathematiker," in *Bibliotheca Mathematica*, 3d series, vol. 2, pp. 326–350 (1901), and other bibliographies published in that journal.

Raymond Clare Archibald "Bibliographia de mathematicis," in *Scripta Mathematica*, vol. 1 (1932), etc.

Finally, in the critical bibliographies published in *Isis* since 1913, mainly in the sections devoted to the nineteenth and twentieth centuries.

Note on Biographical Dictionaries and Encyclopaedias

The following abbreviations which I have used may require explanation:

ADB   *Allgemeine deutsche Biographie.*
DNB   *Dictionary of National Biography.*
DAB   *Dictionary of American Biography.*

These are the three most important dictionaries of national biography available to-day, and their value can hardly be over-estimated. This does not mean that they are faultless; the articles are necessarily unequal, but most of them are signed and include references.

The *ADB* was begun in 1871 and completed in 1910 (Leipzig, 55 vols.). A 56th volume published in 1912 contains a general index. This is periodically complemented by an annual first entitled *Biographisches Jahrbuch und Deutscher Nekrolog* (vol. 1, for 1896; vol. 18, for 1913, published in 1917), and later called *Deutsches biographisches Jahrbuch* (vol. 1 for 1914–16, published in 1925; vol. 11 for 1929, published in 1932). I have not seen vols. 6 to 9 relating to the years 1924 to 1927, and believe that they have not yet been published. Note that the *ADB* contains biographies not only of Germans but of many other people, Dutch-men, Belgians, Danes, Swiss, Poles, whom the editors saw fit to annex.

The *DNB* was begun in 1885, and the last (63d) volume appeared in 1900. It has been reprinted in 21 volumes. A supplement in three volumes, published in 1901 and later reprinted in one volume, brought the series up to date to the end of the nineteenth century; a second supplement, also in three volumes, published in 1912, contains the biographies of people who died from 1901 to 1911; a third supplement covers the period 1912–21. The second and third supplements have been reprinted together under the title, *The twentieth century D.N.B*, with a cumulative index. A 'concise dictionary' wherein the notices are reduced on an average to one-fourteenth of their full length was published in 1917, and the supplements have been abbreviated in the same manner.

The *DAB* began to appear in 1928 and is almost completed (vol. 18, to Trowbridge, 1936).

There are other national biographies, too many to mention. Allow me to make an exception for the *Biographie nationale* of Belgium, the first volume of which appeared in 1866, now nearing completion (vol. 25 to Uyt, 1932). This is an excellent series, of which greater nations might be proud. The French national biography (*Dictionnaire de biographie française*) is still in its initial stage; the first volume began to appear in parts in 1933; the latest part I have seen is fascicle 11, being the fifth of vol. 2, to Anjou (1935).

The best way of beginning any biographical investigation is to turn to such a collection, if available. It is well also to consult encyclopaedias (such as the *Encyclopaedia Britannica*, the *Grande encyclopédie*, the *Enciclopedia italiana*, the *Encyclopaedia Judaica*, etc.), the articles of which are sometimes signed and may include valuable references and other hints. These are simply guide-posts; it is much wiser to use them with due caution than to disregard them. It is advisable to consult first a national encyclopaedia (e.g., a Scandinavian for a Scandinavian; a Russian for a Russian; a Greek for a Greek), in order to know a man's reputation in his own country, and perhaps to obtain information of geographical and genealogical interest and other information derived from local sources; then one or two foreign encyclopaedias, in order to obtain a more neutral judgment and a comparative estimate from the international point of view.

Information on many such collections and cyclopaedias will be found in Loria's *Guida* (Milano, 1916), in C. V. Langlois's *Manuel de bibliographie historique* (Paris, 1901–04), and in other works of the kind.

ABEL, NIELS HENRIK (1802–29).

Carl Anton Bjerknes, *A., tableau de sa vie et de son action scientifique* (Paris, 1885: 368 pp., portr.). *Niels Henrik Abel: Mémorial publié à l'occasion du centenaire de sa naissance* (Kristiania, 1902: 450 pp., portr., facsim.). Charles Lucas de Peslöüan, *A., sa vie et son oeuvre* (Paris, 1906: 184 pp.). Gösta Mittag-Leffler, in *La Revue du mois*, vol. 4, pp. 5–26, 207–229 (1907). Émile Picard, *Mélanges de mathématiques et de physique* (1924), pp. 85–90. Prasad, *Some Great Mathematicians of the Nineteenth Century* (vol. 1, 1933), pp. 111–165.

Oeuvres complètes, edited by L. Sylow and S. Lie (Christiania, 1881, 2 vols.).

ADAMS, JOHN COUCH (1819–92). Celestial mechanics, mathematical physics.

A. M. Clerke, in *DNB*, supp., vol. 1, pp. 15–17 (1901). Macfarlane, *Lectures on Ten British Physicists of the Nineteenth Century* (1919), pp. 119–130.

Scientific Papers, ed. by William Grylls Adams and Ralph Allen Sampson, with a memoir by J. W. L. Glaisher (Cambridge, 1896–1900, 2 vols.).

AIRY, SIR GEORGE BIDDELL (1801–92). Celestial mechanics.

Autobiography, edited by his son Wilfrid Airy (Cambridge, 1896: 426 pp.). Including biographical supplement, bibliography, portrait. A. M. Clerke, in *DNB*, supp., vol. 1, pp. 22–25 (1901). Macfarlane, *British Physicists*, pp. 106–118.

APPELL, PAUL (1855–1930). Analysis, mechanics, theory of functions.

Ernest Lebon, *P.A.* (Paris, 1910: 80 pp., portr.).

Souvenirs d'un Alsacien, 1858–1922 (Paris, 1923: 320 pp.), an autobiography.

Cinquantenaire scientifique de P.A. (Paris, 1927: 47 pp., portr.).

ARONHOLD, SIEGFRIED (1819–84). Theory of invariants.

Emil Lampe, *Die reine Mathematik in den Jahren 1884–1899: Nebst Actenstücken* [pp. 33–48] *zum Leben von S. A.* (Berlin, 1899: 48 pp., portr.). Note by Moritz Cantor in *ADB*, vol. 46, p. 58 (1902).

BABBAGE, CHARLES (1792–1871). Constructor of a mathematical machine, actuary, founder of the Statistical Society, 1834.

Passages from the Life of a Philosopher (London, 1864: 512 pp., portr.), an autobiography.

A. M. Clerke, in *DNB*, vol. 2, pp. 304–306 (1885). John Fyvie, "The Calculating 'Philosopher,'" in his *Some Literary Eccentrics* (London, 1906), pp. 179–209 (with portrait). Macfarlane, *British Physicists*, pp. 71–83.

BACHMANN, PAUL (1837–1920). Theory of numbers.

The fourth part of his monumental "Zahlentheorie," "Die Arithmetik der quadratischen Formen," the printing of which was posthumously completed in 1923, contains a portrait and a biographical sketch by Robert Haussner. See also Haussner's *Zum Gedächtnisse von Paul Bachmann* in the second edition of the latter's *Grundlehren der neueren Zahlentheorie* (Leipzig, 1921). Kurt Hensel: "Bachmann und sein Lebenswerk" (*Jahresbericht der deutschen Mathematiker-Vereinigung*, vol. 36, pp. 31–73, 1927), including portrait and bibliography.

BAIRE, RENÉ (1874–1932). Theory of functions, irrationals, continuity, theory of aggregates.

A. Buhl, in *Enseignement mathématique*, vol. 31, pp. 5–13 (1933).

BALL, SIR ROBERT STAWELL (1840–1913). Theory of screws, dynamics, mathematical astronomy.

Reminiscences and Letters, edited by his son W. Valentine Ball (London, 1915: 424 pp.). Includes a study on R. B.'s mathematical papers by E. T. Whittaker.

BARRÉ DE SAINT-VENANT, see SAINT-VENANT.

BELLAVITIS, GIUSTO (1803–80). Founder of the calculus of equipollences (1835–37), comparable and anterior to the type of calculus developed by Hamilton and Grassmann.

Life and bibliography by Antonio Favaro in *Zeitschrift für Mathematik und Physik*, Hist.-lit. Abtheilung, vol. 26, pp. 153–169 (1881). E. Nestore Legnazzi, *Commemorazione del prof. G. B.* (Padova, 1881).

BELTRAMI, EUGENIO (1835–1900). Non-Euclidean and infinitesimal geometry.

G. Loria, "E. B. e le sue opere matematiche," in *Bibliotheca Mathematica*, 3d series, vol. 2, pp. 392–440 (1901), with portrait. Luigi Bianchi, in *Enciclopedia italiana*, vol. 6, p. 581 (1930).
Opere matematiche (Milano, 1902–20, 4 vols.).

BERTRAND, JOSEPH (1822–1900). Analysis, probabilities, history of science, mathematical physics.

Biographies by Marcelin Berthelot in his *Science et education* (Paris, 1901), pp. 113–139, by Gaston Darboux in *Mémoires of the Académie des Sciences*, vol. 47, pp. 321–386 (1904), and by H. Poincaré, *Savants et écrivains* (1910), pp. 157–161.

Bertrand's *Éloges académiques*, nouvelle série (Paris, 1902), contains a biography by Darboux (pp. vii–li) and a bibliography of Bertrand's writings (pp. 387–399).

BESSEL, FRIEDRICH WILHELM (1784–1846). Celestial mechanics.

J. F. Encke, "Gedächtnissrede auf B.," in the *Abhandlungen* of the Berlin Akademie der Wissenschaften, 1846, pp. xxi–xlii. J. F. W. Herschel, *A Brief Notice of the Life, Researches, and Discoveries of F. W. B.* (London, 1847: 16 pp.). August Ludwig Busch, "Verzeichniss sämmtlicher Werke, Abhandlungen, Aufsätze und Bemerkungen von F. W. B.," in *Astronomische Beobachtungen auf der Königlichen Universitäts-Sternwarte in Königsberg*, pt. 24, pp. xxi–lviii (1848).

Abhandlungen, ed. by Rudolf Engelmann (Leipzig, 1875–76, 3 vols.). *Populäre Vorlesungen*, ed. by H. C. Schumacher (Hamburg, 1848: 654 pp.).

Briefwechsel zwischen Gauss und Bessel (Leipzig, 1880: 623 pp.). *Briefwechsel zwischen W. Olbers und F. W. Bessel*, ed. by Adolf

Erman (Leipzig, 1852, 2 vols.). Including short biographies of both.

BETTI, ENRICO (1823–92). Algebraic equations, elliptic functions, mathematical physics, analysis situs.

Vito Volterra, *Saggi scientifici* (Bologna, 1920), pp. 35, 55 ff. F. Enriques in *Enciclopedia italiana*, vol. 6, p. 834 (1930). *Opere matematiche* (Milano, 1903–13, 2 vols.). With bibliography and portrait.

BOLTZMANN, LUDWIG (1844–1906). Mathematical physics, principles of mechanics.

Festschrift L. B. gewidmet zum sechzigsten Geburtstage, ed. by Stefan Meyer (Leipzig, 1904: 942 pp., portr., 101 fig., 2 pl.). Anton Lampa, in *Biographisches Jahrbuch*, vol. 11, pp. 96–104 (1908). Johannes Classen, *Vorlesungen über moderne Naturphilosophen*, pp. 108–128 (Hamburg, 1908).

Wissenschaftliche Abhandlungen, ed. by Fritz Hasenöhrl (Leipzig, 1909, 3 vols.). Portrait in vol. 3. *Populäre Schriften* (Leipzig, 1905: 446 pp.).

BÓLYAI DE BOLYA, FARKAS (1775–1856), and his son BÓLYAI, JÁNOS (1802–60). Non-Euclidean geometry.

Franz Schmidt, "Aus dem Leben zweier ungarischer Mathematiker Johann und Wolfgang Bolyai von Bolya," in Grunert's *Archiv der Mathematik und Physik*, vol. 48, pp. 217–228 (1868). In French in the *Mémoires* of the Société des Sciences Physiques et Naturelles de Bordeaux, vol. 5, pp. 191–205 (1867), and in János Bólyai, *La science absolue de l'espace* (Paris, 1868), pp. 7–21. *Libellus post Saeculum quam I. B. . . . Claudiopoli natus est ad celebrandam Memoriam eius Immortalem*, ed. by Ludwig Schlesinger (Cluj, 1902; 170 pp., facs.). Ludwig Schlesinger, "Neue Beiträge zur Biographie von Wolfgang und Johann Bolyai," in *Bibliotheca Mathematica*, 3d series, vol. 4, pp. 260–270 (1903). Ludwig Schlesinger, "Johann Bolyai: Festrede," in Deutsche Mathematiker-Vereinigung, *Jahresbericht*, vol. 12, pp. 165–194 (1903). Wolfgang and Johann Bolyai, *Geometrische Untersuchungen*, ed. by Paul Stäckel (Leipzig, 1913). I. Leben und Schriften der beiden B. II. Stücke aus den Schriften der beiden B.

Briefwechsel zwischen Carl Friedrich Gauss und Wolfgang Bolyai, ed. by Franz Schmidt and Paul Stäckel (Leipzig, 1899: 220 pp., 2 pl., 14 facs.).

BOLZANO, BERNARD (1781–1848). Principles of analysis, theory of functions.

Hugo Bergmann, *Das philosophische Werk B. B.* (Halle a. S., 1909: 244 pp.). Ruth Struik and D. J. Struik, "Cauchy and B. in Prague," in *Isis*, vol. 11, pp. 364–366 (1928). Heinrich Fels, *B. B., sein Leben und sein Werk* (Leipzig, 1929: 119 pp.).

The publication of his complete works (*Schriften*) was begun by the Königliche Böhmische Gesellschaft der Wissenschaften in Prague in 1930 (*Isis*, vol. 15, pp. 353–355); vol. 2, 1931 (*Isis*, vol. 19, p. 405); vol. 3, 1932 (*Isis*, vol. 19, pp. 404–405); vol. 4, 1935. *Wissenschaftslehre* (Leipzig, 1929–31, 4 vols.; cf. *Isis*, vol. 18, p. 470).

BOOLE, GEORGE (1815–64). One of the founders of mathematical logic.

John Venn, in *DNB*, vol. 5, pp. 369–370 (1886). Macfarlane, *Lectures on Ten British Mathematicians of the Nineteenth Century*, pp. 50–63.
Collected Logical Works. Vol. 1 not yet published; vol. 2, The Laws of Thought (Chicago, 1916; out of print).

BORCHARDT, KARL WILHELM (1817–80). Theory of determinants, theta functions.

Note by M. Cantor, in *ADB*, vol. 47, p. 112 (1903).
Gesammelte Werke, edited by G. Hettner (Berlin, 1888: 512 pp., portr.).

BRIOSCHI, FRANCESCO (1824–97). Theory of invariants, elliptic and hyperelliptic functions, theory of surfaces, mechanics.

Eugenio Beltrami, "F. B.," in *Annali di matematica*, serie 2, vol. 26, pp. 343–347 (1897). E. Pascal, *Pochi cenni su F. B.* (Milano, 1898). Giulio Vivanti, in *Enciclopedia italiana*, vol. 7, p. 868 (1930). Prasad (1934), pp. 94–115.
Opere matematiche (Milano, 1901–09, 5 vols.).

CANTOR, GEORG (1845–1918). Theory of aggregates.

Adolf Fraenkel, "G. C.," in Deutsche Mathematiker Vereinigung, *Jahresbericht*, vol. 39, pp. 189–266 (1930), with portrait, also in *Encyclopaedia Judaica*, vol. 5, pp. 28–29 (1930). Prasad (1934), pp. 183–211.

Gesammelte Abhandlungen: Mit Anmerkungen sowie mit Ergänzungen aus dem Briefwechsel Cantor-Dedekind, ed. by Ernst Zermelo (Berlin, 1932: 494 pp., portr.). Includes a biography by Adolf Fraenkel. See also *Isis*, vol. 3, p. 343.

CARNOT, LAZARE (1753–1823). Geometry of position (1803), principles of analysis and mechanics.

Obituary by Arago; English translation in *Biographies of Distinguished Scientific Men* (1857), pp. 287–361. Mathieu Noel Rioust, *C.* (Gand, 1817). First printed in Paris, 1817, and suppressed by the police, reprinted in Brussels, then in Ghent, in the same year. Wilhelm Körte, *Das Leben L. N. M. Carnots: Mit einem Anhange enthaltend die ungedruckten Poesien Carnots* (Leipzig, 1820: 490 pp.). Hippolyte Carnot (1801–88), *Mémoires sur C. par son fils* (Paris, 1861–63, 2 vols.). Includes a bibliography; the covers are dated 1869! New edition (Paris, 1893, 2 vols.). *Centenaire de L. C., notes et documents inédits* (Paris, 1923). Includes a bibliography and portraits. Cf. *Isis*, vol. 3, p. 116; vol. 4, p. 594.

Correspondance générale [1792–95], ed. by Étienne Charavay (1892–1907, 4 vols.). This, of course, is chiefly political.

CAUCHY, AUGUSTIN (1789–1857). Reorganization of analysis.

Claude Alphonse Valson, *La vie et les travaux du baron C.* (Paris, 1868, 2 vols.). F. J. Studnička, *C. als formaler Begründer der Determinantentheorie* (Prag, 1876: 40 pp.). Notice by Joseph Bertrand, read at the Académie des Sciences, 1898, and reprinted in his *Éloges académiques*, nouvelle série, pp. 101–120 (Paris, 1902). Philip E. B. Jourdain, "The Origin of C.'s Conceptions of a Definite Integral and of the Continuity of a Function," in *Isis*, vol. 1, pp. 661–703 (1914). Ruth Struik and D. J. Struik, "C. and Bolzano in Prague," in *Isis*, vol. 11, pp. 364–366 (1928). Maurice d'Ocagne, *Hommes et choses de science* (Paris, 1930), pp. 111–125. Prasad (1933), pp. 68–110.

Oeuvres complètes (Paris, 1882–   , 24 vols. to date. Three more volumes are scheduled to appear).

CAYLEY, ARTHUR (1821–95). Theory of invariants.

A. R. Forsyth, in *DNB*, supp., vol. 1, pp. 401–402 (1901). Macfarlane, *British Mathematicians*, pp. 64–77. Prasad (1934), pp. 1–33.
Collected Mathematical Papers (Cambridge, 1889–98, 14 vols.). Including a biography by A. R. Forsyth in vol. 8, and portraits in vols. 6, 7, 11. *Briefwechsel von L. Schläfli mit A. Cayley*, ed. by J. H. Graf, in Naturforschende Gesellschaft, Bern, *Mittheilungen*, 1905.

CHASLES, MICHEL (1793–1880). Synthetic geometry.

Notice by Bertrand read at the Académie des Sciences in 1892 and reprinted in his *Éloges académiques*, nouvelle série, pp. 27–58 (1902). Paul Tannery, *Mémoires scientifiques*, vol. 6, pp. 517–521 (1926). Gino Loria, "M. C. e la teoria delle sezzione coniche," in *Osiris*, vol. 1, pp. 412–441 (1936), with portrait.
Chasles's papers are preserved in the archives of the Académie des sciences.

CHEBYSHEV, PAFNUTII L'VOVICH (1821–94). Theory of numbers.

A. Vassilief, "Pafnutii Lvovitch Tchébychef et son oeuvre scientifique," in Loria's *Bollettino di bibliografia e storia delle scienze matematiche*, vol. 1, pp. 33–45, 81–92, 113–139 (Torino, 1898). Also in German (Leipzig, 1900).
Oeuvres, ed. by A. Markoff and N. Sonin (St.-Pétersbourg, 1899–1907, 2 vols.). With a biography by C. A. Possé and portraits.

CLAUSIUS, RUDOLF (1822–88). Mathematical physics, chiefly thermodynamics, potential.

Eduard Riecke, *R. C.* (Göttingen, 1888: 40 pp.). Includes a bibliography. George Francis Fitzgerald in Royal Society of London, *Proceedings*, vol. 48, pp. i–viii (1890). F. Folie, "R. C., sa vie, ses travaux et leur portée métaphysique," in *Revue des questions scientifiques*, vol. 27, pp. 419–487 (Bruxelles, 1890). Notice by Josiah Willard Gibbs, *Scientific Papers* (London, 1906, vol. 2, pp. 261–267). Max Reinganum, in *ADB*, vol. 55, pp. 720–729 (1910).

CLEBSCH, ALFRED (1833–72). Theory of curves and surfaces, geometrical applications of Abelian functions, invariants, representation of one surface upon another, mathematical physics.

Obituary by C. Neumann in the Göttingen Gesellschaft der Wissenschaften, *Nachrichten*, 1872, pp. 550–559.

Vorlesungen über Geometrie, ed. by Ferdinand Lindemann (Leipzig, 1876–91, 2 vols.; revised ed., 1906–32). French translation by Adolphe Benoist (Paris, 1879–83, 3 vols.).

CLERK-MAXWELL, see MAXWELL.

CLIFFORD, WILLIAM KINGDON (1845–79). Synthetic geometry, metaphysics, philosophy of science.

Leslie Stephen, in *DNB*, vol. 11, pp. 82–85 (1887). Macfarlane, *British Mathematicians*, pp. 78–91.

Lectures and Essays, ed. by Leslie Stephen and Frederick Pollock (London, 1879, 2 vols., portr.). Including a short biographical sketch. *Mathematical Fragments, being Facsimiles of his Unfinished Papers Relating to the Theory of Graphs* (lithographed, London, 1881). *Mathematical Papers*, ed. by Robert Tucker (London, 1882: 728 pp.). With introduction by H. J. S. Smith.

COURNOT, ANTOINE AUGUSTIN (1801–77). Probabilities, pioneer application of mathematics to political economy, history and philosophy of mathematics and of science.

Souvenirs d'A. Cournot, 1760–1860; précédés d'un introduction par E. P. Bottinelli (Paris, 1913: 302 pp.).

Special number of the *Revue de métaphysique et de morale* (May, 1905) devoted to him. Gaston Milhaud, "Le hasard chez Aristote et chez C.," "La raison chez C.," in his *Études sur la pensée scientifique chez les Grecs et chez les modernes* (Paris, 1906), pp. 137–176. François Mentré, *C. et la renaissance du probabilisme au XIXᵉ siècle* (Paris, 1908: 658 pp.). J. Segond, *C. et la psychologie vitaliste* (Paris, 1910). Georges Loiseau, *Les doctrines économiques de C.* (Paris, 1913). E. P. Bottinelli, *A. C., métaphysicien de la connaissance* (Paris, 1913). F. Y. Edgeworth, in *Palgrave's Dictionary of Political Economy*, vol. 1, pp. 445–447 (1925). F. Mentré, *Pour qu'on lise Cournot* (Paris, 1927). Lilly Hecht, *A. C. und L. Walras* (Heidelberg, 1930: 93 pp.). R. Ruyer, *L'humanité de l'avenir d'après C.* (Paris, 1930). François Bompaire, *Du principe de liberté économique dans l'oeuvre de C. et dans celle de l'école de Lausanne* (*Walras, Pareto*) (Paris, 1931: 740 pp.). René Roy, "C. et l'école mathématique," in *Econometrica*, vol. 1, pp. 13–22, portr. (1933).

COUTURAT, LOUIS (1868–1914).   Mathematical logic.

Louis Couturat (Coulommiers, n.d.: 69 pp.). Includes obituaries by Louis Benaerts, Arnold Reymond, André Lalande, Xavier Léon, and L. de Beaufront, and a bibliography. The brochure is undated, but it appeared after July, 1915, probably before the end of that year (*Isis*, vol. 3, p. 121).

CREMONA, LUIGI (1830–1903).   Synthetic geometry.

Gino Loria, "L. C. et son oeuvre mathématique," in *Bibliotheca Mathematica*, 3d series, vol. 5, pp. 125–195 (1904). Eugenio Bertini, in *Enciclopedia italiana*, vol. 11, p. 830 (1931). Prasad, (1934), pp. 116–143.

Opere matematiche (Milano, 1914–17, 3 vols.). The third volume contains a biography by Bertini; portrait in vol. 1.

DARBOUX, GASTON (1842–1917).   General theory of surfaces.

Ernest Lebon, *G. D.* (Paris, 1910, 80 pp.; rev. ed., 1913, 97 pp.). Biography, bibliography, portrait. *Éloges académiques et discours*, published by the Comité du Jubilé scientifique de M. Gaston Darboux (Paris, 1912), contains an account of the jubilee (pp. 441–524) and a portrait. Notice by Émile Picard, read at the public annual session of the Académie des Sciences, December 10, 1917, reprinted in his *Discours et mélanges* (Paris, 1922), pp. 75–106. David Hilbert, "G. D.," in Göttingen Gesellschaft der Wissenschaften, *Nachrichten*, Geschäftliche Mitteilungen, 1917, pp. 70–75. L. P. Eisenhart, "D.'s Contribution to Geometry," in American Mathematical Society, *Bulletin*, vol. 24, pp. 227–237 (1918). Prasad (1934), pp. 143–182. *Isis*, vol. 3, p. 121; vol. 4, p. 163; vol. 5, p. 248.

DARWIN, SIR GEORGE HOWARD (1845–1912).   Figure of the earth, tides.

James Hopwood Jeans, in *DNB*, 1912–21, pp. 144–146 (1927). *Isis*, vol. 1, pp. 166, 311, 560; vol. 5, p. 248.

Scientific papers (Cambridge, 1907–16, 5 vols.). Vol. 5 includes biographies by Sir Francis Darwin and E. W. Brown and portrait.

DEDEKIND, RICHARD (1831–1916). Theory of irrationals.

Festschrift zur Feier des siebzigsten Geburtstages von R. D. (Braunschweig, 1901: 254 pp.). *Isis*, vol. 4, p. 163.

Gesammelte mathematische Werke, ed. by Robert Fricke, Emmy Noether, Öystein Ore (Braunschweig, 1930–32, 3 vols.).

DE MORGAN, AUGUSTUS (1806–71). Algebra, mathematical logic.

Memoir of A. D. M. by his wife Sophia Elizabeth De Morgan, with Selections from his Letters (London, 1882: 432 pp., portr.). Leslie Stephen, in *DNB*, vol. 14, pp. 331–334 (1888). Macfarlane, *British Mathematicians*, pp. 19–33.

DIRICHLET, GUSTAV LEJEUNE (1805–59). Theory of numbers, definite integrals, Fourier series, attraction of ellipsoids.

E. E. Kummer, "Gedächtnissrede auf Gustav Peter Lejeune Dirichlet," in Akademie der Wissenschaften zu Berlin, *Abhandlungen*, 1861, pp. 1–36. M. Cantor, in *ADB*, vol. 5, pp. 251–252 (1877).

Werke, ed. by L. Kronecker and L. Fuchs (Berlin, 1889–97, 2 vols.). "Briefwechsel zwischen G. L. D. und Leopold Kronecker," ed. by Ernst Schering, in Göttingen Gesellschaft der Wissenschaften, *Nachrichten*, 1885, pp. 361–382. "Correspondance entre Liouville et Dirichlet," ed. by Jules Tannery, in *Bulletin des sciences mathématiques*, deuxième série, vol. 32, pt. 1, pp. 47–62, 88–95 (1908); vol. 33, pt. 1, pp. 47–64 (1909).

EDGEWORTH, FRANCIS YSIDRO (1845–1926). Probabilities, econometry, 'mathematical psychics.'

A. L. Bowley, *F. Y. E.'s Contributions to Mathematical Statistics* (London, 1928: 146 pp.). A. L. Bowley, "F. Y. E.," in *Econometrica*, vol. 2, pp. 113–124, with portrait (1934).

Papers Relating to Political Economy (London, 1925, 3 vols.).

EISENSTEIN, GOTTHOLD (1823–52). Theory of numbers, elliptic functions. "There have been only three great mathematicians, Archimedes, Newton, and Eisenstein!" Who said that? Gauss!

Note by M. Cantor in *ADB*, vol. 5, p. 774 (1877).

Mathematische Abhandlungen, besonders aus dem Gebiete der höhern Arithmetik und der elliptischen Functionen (Berlin, 1847: 344 pp.). Preface by Gauss. "Briefe von ,G. E. an M. A. Stern," ed. by A. Hurwitz, in *Abhandlungen zur Geschichte der mathematischen Wissenschaften*, Heft 7, pp. 169–203 (1895).

ENCKE, JOHANN FRANZ (1791–1865). Celestial mechanics.

Karl Bruhns, *J. F. E., sein Leben und Wirken* (Leipzig, 1869: 360 pp., portr.). Karl Bruhns, in *ADB*, vol. 6, pp. 99–103 (1877).

Gesammelte mathematische und astronomische Abhandlungen, ed. by Harry Gravelius (Berlin, 1888–89, 3 vols.).

FIEDLER, OTTO WILHELM (1832–1912). 'Cyclography,' descriptive geometry and its relationship to synthetic geometry.

Wilhelm Fiedler, "Meine Mitarbeit an der Reform der darstellenden Geometrie in neuerer Zeit," in Deutsche Mathematiker-Vereinigung, *Jahresbericht*, vol. 14, pp. 493–503 (1905). A. Voss, "W. F.," in Deutsche Mathematiker, Vereinigung, *Jahresbericht*, vol. 22, pp. 97–113, with portrait (1913). Ernst Fiedler, in *Biographisches Jahrbuch*, vol. 17, pp. 14–25 (1915).

FOURIER, JOSEPH (1768–1830). Analytical theory of heat, Fourier's series, 1822.

François Arago, "J. F." (read in 1833), *Oeuvres complètes*, vol. 1, pp. 295–369 (1854). English translation in *Biographies of Distinguished Scientific Men*, pp. 242–286 (1857), reprinted in Smithsonian Institution, *Annual Report*, 1871, pp. 137–176. Léon Sagnet, in *Grande encyclopédie*, vol. 17, pp. 908–909 (1893).

Oeuvres, edited by G. Darboux (Paris, 1888–90, 2 vols.). With bibliography and portrait.

FREDHOLM, ERIC IVAR (1866–1927). Integral equations.

Nils Zeilow, "I. F.," in *Acta Mathematica*, vol. 54, pp. i–xvi, with facsimile (1930). Ugo Amaldi, in *Enciclopedia italiana*, vol. 16, p. 49 (1932).

FREGE, GOTTLOB (1848–1925). Mathematical logic, foundations of arithmetic.

Wilma Papst, *G. F. als Philosoph* (Berlin, 1932?: 51 pp.).

FRESNEL, AUGUSTIN (1788–1827). Wave theory of light, optical surfaces.

Notice by Arago, read in 1830; in English in *Biographies of Distinguished Scientific Men* (1857), pp. 399–471. Émile Picard, *Cérémonie du centenaire de la mort de Fresnel* (Paris, 1927: 35 pp.). Louis de Broglie, *Recueil d'exposés sur les ondes et corpuscules* (Paris, 1930), pp. 1–26.

Oeuvres complètes, ed. by Henri de Senarmont, Émile Verdet, and Léonor Fresnel (Paris, 1866–70, 3 vols.). *Isis*, vol. 4, p. 155; vol. 9, p. 170.

FUCHS, LAZARUS (1833–1902). Linear differential equations.

Gesammelte mathematische Werke, ed. by Richard Fuchs and Ludwig Schlesinger (Berlin, 1904–09, 3 vols., portr.).

GALOIS, ÉVARISTE (1811–32). Groups of substitution.

Paul Dupuy, "La vie d'É. G.," in *Annales de l'École Normale Supérieure*, 3ᵉ série, vol. 13, pp. 197–266 (1896), with portrait. Reprinted in Charles Péguy's *Cahiers de la quinzaine*, 5ᵉ série, 2ᵉ cahier, 104 pp., with portrait (Paris, 1903). Abbreviated in English by G. Sarton in the *Scientific Monthly*, vol. 13, pp. 363–375 (New York, 1921).

Oeuvres mathématiques, ed. by Émile Picard (Paris, 1897: 74 pp.). "Manuscrits et papiers inédits de G.," ed. by Jules Tannery, in *Bulletin des sciences mathématiques*, deuxième série, vol. 30, pt. 1, pp. 226–248 (1906); vol. 31, pt. 1, pp. 275–308 (1907).

GAUSS, CARL FRIEDRICH (1777–1855).

Wolfgang Sartorius, *G. zum Gedächtniss* (Leipzig, 1856). Adolphe Quetelet, *Sciences mathématiques et physiques chez les Belges* (Bruxelles, 1866), pp. 643–655. F. A. T. Winnecke, *G., ein Umriss seines Lebens und Wirkens* (Braunschweig, 1877). Theodor Wittstein, *G.* (Hannover, 1877). Ernst Schering, *G's Geburtstag nach hundertjähriger Wiederkehr* (Göttingen, 1877: 40 pp.). Ludwig Hänselmann, *K. F. G., zwölf Kapitel aus seinem Leben* (Leipzig, 1878: 110 pp.). *Festschrift zur Feier der Enthüllung des Gauss-Weber-Denkmals in Göttingen* (Leipzig, 1899: 204 pp.). Felix Klein and others, *Materialien für eine wissenschaftliche Biographie von G.* (Leipzig, 1911–20, 8 vols.; cf. *Isis*, vol. 4, p. 154). Heinrich Mack,

C. F. G. und die Seinen: Festschrift zu seinem 150. Geburtstage (Braunschweig, 1927: 162 pp., 12 pl.). Prasad (1933), pp. 1–67. *Werke* (Leipzig, 1866–1933, 12 vols.). *Isis*, vol. 20, p. 559. "Gauss' wissenschaftliches Tagebuch, 1796–1814," ed. by F. Klein, in Göttingen Gesellschaft der Wissenschaften, *Festschrift* (Berlin, 1901), pp. 1–44, with portr. and fac. *Briefwechsel zwischen C. F. G. und H. C. Schumacher*, ed. by C. A. Peters (Altona, 1860–65, 6 vols.). *Briefe zwischen A. von Humboldt und G.* (Leipzig, 1877: 79 pp.). *Briefe von C. F. G. an B. Nicolai* (Karlsruhe, 1877: 36 pp.). *Briefwechsel zwischen G. und Bessel* (Berlin, 1880: 623 pp.). *Briefwechsel zwischen C. F. G. und Wolfgang Bolyai*, ed. by Franz Schmidt und Paul Stäckel (Leipzig, 1899: 224 pp.). *Briefwechsel zwischen Olbers und G.*, ed. by C. Schilling and I. Kramer (Berlin, 1900). *Briefwechsel zwischen C. F. G. und Christian Ludwig Gerling*, ed. by Clemens Schaefer (Berlin, 1927: 840 pp.). *Isis*, vol. 11, p. 197.

GERMAIN, SOPHIE (1776–1831). Elastic surfaces, curvature of surfaces, theory of numbers.

Cinq lettres de S. G. à C. F. Gauss, ed. by B. Boncompagni (Berlin, 1880). Georg Biedenkapp, *S. G., ein weiblicher Denker* (Jena, 1910).

Oeuvres philosophiques, suivies de pensées et de lettres inédites et précédées d'une notice sur sa vie et ses oeuvres par H[ippoly]te Stupuy (Paris, 1879, 375 pp.; new ed., 1896, 411 pp., portr.).

GIBBS, JOSIAH WILLARD (1839–1903). Thermodynamics, equilibrium of chemical systems, vector analysis.

Henry A. Bumstead, "J. W. G.," in *American Journal of Science*, 4th series, vol. 16, pp. 187–202, with portr. (Sept., 1903). Reprinted in Gibbs's *Collected Works*. Pierre Duhem, *J.-W. G.* (Paris, 1908: 44 pp.). Frederick George Donnan, *The Influence of J. W. G. on the Science of Physical Chemistry* (Philadelphia, 1924: 29 pp.). E. B. Wilson, in *DAB*, vol. 7, pp. 248–251 (1931). *Scientific Papers* (London, 1906, 2 vols.). *Collected Works*, ed. by W. R. Longley and R. G. Van Name (New York, 1928, 2 vols., portr.). This is more complete than *Scientific Papers*. On a proposed new edition and commentary see *Nature*, vol. 121, pp. 245–246 (1928); *Isis*, vol. 11, p. 476.

Göpel, Adolf (1812–47). Abelian and theta functions.

M. Cantor, in *ADB*, vol. 9, p. 370 (1879). Short notes by C. G. J. Jacobi and A. L. Crelle in Crelle's *Journal für die reine und angewandte Mathematik*, vol. 35, pp. 313–318 (1847), reprinted in the German translation of Göpel's *Theoriae transcendentium Abelianarum primi ordinis adumbratio levis* (1847) in Ostwald's *Klassiker der exakten Wissenschaften*, no. 67 (Leipzig, 1895: 60 pp.), pp. 52–58.

Gordan, Paul (1837–1912). Theory of invariants.

Giovanni Lampariello, in *Enciclopedia italiana*, vol. 17, p. 547 (1933).

Grassmann, Hermann (1809–77). *Ausdehnungslehre*.

Victor Schlegel, *H. G., sein Leben und seine Werke* (Leipzig, 1878), with a bibliography. Moritz Cantor and August Leskien, in *ADB*, vol. 9, pp. 595–598 (1879).

Gesammelte mathematische und physikalische Werke (Leipzig, 1894–1911, 3 vols. in 6). The second part of vol. 3 contains a biography by Friedrich Engel (1911) and a bibliography of Grassmann's published and unpublished writings.

Green, George (1793–1841). Potential function, theory of electricity and magnetism.

Max Bacharach, *Abriss der Geschichte der Potentialtheorie* (Göttingen, 1883: 78 pp.). G. J. Gray, in *DNB*, vol. 23, pp. 42–43 (1890).

Mathematical Papers, ed. by Norman Macleod Ferrers (London, 1871: 346 pp.). Including a brief memoir by the editor.

Halphen, Georges Henri (1844–89). Geometry of curves and surfaces, elliptic functions.

Léon Sagnet, in *Grande encyclopédie*, vol. 19, pp. 778–779 (1894). H. Poincaré, *Savants et écrivains*, pp. 125–140. Émile Picard, *Mélanges de mathématiques et de physique*, pp. 1–11.

Oeuvres, ed. by C. Jordan, H. Poincaré, É. Picard, with the help of E. Vessiot (Paris, 1916–24, 4 vols.).

HAMILTON, SIR WILLIAM ROWAN (1805–65). Wave theory, dynamics, quaternions.

Robert Perceval Graves, *Life of Sir W. R. H.* (London, 1882–89, 3 vols., with portrs.). Macfarlane, *British Mathematicians*, pp. 34–49.
Mathematical Papers, ed. by A. W. Conway and J. L. Synge, vol. 1 (Cambridge, 1931: 534 pp.).

HELMHOLTZ, HERMANN VON (1821–94). Mathematical physics.

Leo Königsberger, *H. v. H.* (Braunschweig, 1902–03, 3 vols.). Wilhelm Wien, "Hydrodynamische Untersuchungen von H. v. H.," in the *Sitzungsberichte* of the Prussian Academy, 1904, pp. 716–736. Johannes Classen, "Helmholtz, Boltzmann, Poincaré," in his *Vorlesungen über moderne Naturphilosophen* (Hamburg, 1908), pp. 108–128. W. Ostwald, *Grosse Männer* (Leipzig, 1909), pp. 256–310.

Wissenschaftliche Abhandlungen (Leipzig, 1882–95, 3 vols.). *Populäre wissenschaftliche Vorträge* (Braunschweig, 1865–71, 2 vols.). Englished by E. Atkinson (London, 1873–81, 2 vols.). *Schriften zur Erkenntnistheorie*, ed. by Paul Hertz and Moritz Schlick (Berlin, 1921).

HERMITE, CHARLES (1822–1901). Algebra and analysis, theory of functions, elliptic functions.

Camille Jordan, "C. H.," in *Revue scientifique*, 4e série, vol. 15, pp. 129–131 (1901). M. Noether, "C. H.," in *Mathematische Annalen*, vol. 55, pp. 337–385 (1901). É. Picard, "L'oeuvre scientifique de C. H.," in École Normale Supérieure, *Annales scientifiques*, 3e série, vol. 18, pp. 9–34, portr. (1901). H. Poincaré, *Savants et écrivains*, pp. 97–101. E. Picard, *Mélanges de mathématiques et de physique* (1924), pp. 53–84, 121–125. Gaston Darboux, *Éloges académiques et discours* (Paris, 1912), pp. 116–172. Prasad (1934), pp. 34–59.

Oeuvres, edited by his son-in-law Émile Picard (Paris, 1905–17, 4 vols.). Includes biographical preface and portraits. *Correspondance d'H. et de Stieltjes*, ed. by B. Baillaud and H. Bourget (Paris, 1905, 2 vols.).

HERTZ, HEINRICH (1857–94). Principles of mechanics, mathematical physics.

Sir Oliver Lodge, *The Work of H. and some of his Successors* (London, 1894, reprinted from the *Electrician*: 58 pp., portr.). Richard Manno, *H. .H. für die Willensfreiheit? Eine kritische Studie über Mechanismus und Willensfreiheit* (Leipzig, 1900: 72 pp.). Rob. Knott, in *ADB*, vol. 50, pp. 256–259 (1905). Johanna Hertz, *H. H., Erinnerungen, Briefe, Tagebücher* (Leipzig, 1927: 270 pp., 10 pl.).

Gesammelte Werke (Leipzig, 1894–95, 3 vols.). *Gesammelte Abhandlungen* (Leipzig, 1905). *Miscellaneous Papers* (London, 1896).

HESSE, LUDWIG OTTO (1811–74). Analytic and synthetic geometry, theory of surfaces, and invariants ('Hessian').

Gustav Bauer, *Gedächtnissrede auf O. H.* (München, 1882: 36 pp.). C. W. Borchardt, "O. H.," in *Journal für die reine und angewandte Mathematik*, vol. 79, pp. 345–347 (1875). F. Klein, "O. H.," in Polytechnische Schule, Munich, *Bericht*, 1875, pp. 46–50. M. Noether, "O. H.," in *Zeitschrift für Mathematik und Physik*, vol. 20, hist.-lit. Abtheilung, pp. 77–88 (1875). M. Cantor in *ADB*, vol. 12, pp. 306–307 (1880).

Gesammelte Werke (München, 1897: 740 pp.). With biography, bibliography, and portrait.

HILL, GEORGE WILLIAM (1838–1914). Celestial mechanics, lunar theory.

E. W. Brown, in *DAB*, vol. 9, pp. 32–33 (1932).
Collected Mathematical Works (Washington, 1905–07, 4 vols.). Biography by H. Poincaré, portrait.

IVORY, SIR JAMES (1765–1842). Gravitational attraction of ellipsoids, refraction of light.

R. E. Anderson, in *DNB*, vol. 29, p. 82 (1892).

JACOBI, CARL GUSTAV JACOB (1804–51).

Leo Königsberger, *C. G. J. J.* (Leipzig, 1904: 572 pp., portr.). Wilhelm Ahrens, "Ein Beitrag zur Biographie C. G. J. Jacobis," in *Bibliotheca Mathematica*, 3d series, vol. 7, pp. 157–192 (1906); and *J. als Politiker* (Leipzig, 1907: 45 pp.). Ahrens's second paper is only an enlarged edition of the first. Prasad (1933), pp. 166–219.

Viri Doctissimi Clarissimi nuper defuncti C. G. J. Jacobii Catalogus Librorum qui Pretiis appositis venduntur ab A. Asher & Co., Berolini (Paris, 1851: 43 pp.).

Gesammelte Werke (Berlin, 1881–91, 8 vols.). With biography by Lejeune Dirichlet, bibliography, and portrait.

"Correspondance mathématique entre Legendre et Jacobi," in *Journal für die reine und angewandte Mathematik*, vol. 80, pp. 205–279 (1875). *Briefwechsel zwischen C. G. J. Jacobi und M. H. Jacobi*, ed. by Wilhelm Ahrens (*Abhandlungen zur Geschichte der mathematischen Wissenschaften*, Heft 22, 1907: 302 pp.). *Der Briefwechsel zwischen C. G. J. J. und P. H. v. Fuss über die Herausgabe der Werke Leonhard Eulers*, ed. by Paul Stäckel and W. Ahrens (Leipzig, 1908: 195 pp.).

JEVONS, WILLIAM STANLEY (1835–82). Econometry, mathematical logic, principles of science.

Letters and Journal, ed. by his wife (London, 1886), with portrait. A. W. Ward, in *DNB*, vol. 29, pp. 374–378 (1892). "W. S. J.," by Herbert Stanley Jevons and H. Winefrid Jevons, in *Econometrica*, vol. 2, pp. 225–237 (1934).
Methods of Social Reform and other Papers (London, 1883: 391 pp.). *Investigations in Currency and Finance*, ed. by H. S. Foxwell (London, 1884, 472 pp.; 2d ed., abridged, 1909).

JORDAN, CAMILLE (1838–1922). General analysis, substitutions and algebraic equations.

Henri Lebesgue, *Notice sur la vie et les travaux de C. J.* (Paris, 1923: 28 pp., portr.).

KELVIN, LORD (SIR WILLIAM THOMSON, FIRST BARON KELVIN) (1824–1907). Mathematical physics.

Elizabeth (Thomson) King, *Lord K.'s Early Home* (London, 1909: 257 pp.), with portrait. Silvanus Phillips Thompson, *Life of W. T.* (London, 1910, 2 vols.). David Wilson, *W. T. (Lord Kelvin), his Way of Teaching Natural Philosophy* (Glasgow, 1910: 56 pp.). H. Poincaré, *Savants et écrivains* (1910), pp. 213–244. Macfarlane, *British Physicists*, pp. 55–70. Émile Picard, *Discours et mélanges* (1922), pp. 41–73. David Murray, *Lord K. as Professor in the Old College of Glasgow* (Glasgow, 1924: 24 pp.), with portrait.
Mathematical and Physical Papers (Cambridge, 1882–1911, 6 vols.). Vols. 4 to 6 ed. by Sir Joseph Larmor. *Popular Lectures and Addresses* (London, 1889–94, 3 vols.).

KIRCHHOFF, GUSTAV (1824–87). Mathematical physics.

Ludwig Boltzmann, *Populäre Schriften* (Leipzig, 1905), pp. 51–75. W. Voigt, *Zum Gedächtniss von G. K.* (Göttingen, 1888: 10 pp.). R. Knott, in *ADB*, vol. 51, pp. 165–167 (1906).

Gesammelte Abhandlungen (Leipzig, 1882), with portr. *Nachtrag* to the same, ed. by Ludwig Boltzmann (Leipzig, 1891).

KLEIN, FELIX (1849–1925).

"Lebensbilder von eigener Hand," in Universitätsband, Göttingen, *Mitteilungen*, vol. 5, pp. 11–36 (1923). Richard Courant, "F. K. als wissenschaftlicher Führer," in Göttingen Gesellschaft der Wissenschaften, *Nachrichten*, Geschäftliche Mitteilungen, 1925–26, pp. 39–46. Prasad (1934), pp. 245–277.

Gesammelte mathematische Abhandlungen, ed. by Robert Fricke and A. Ostrowski (Berlin, 1921–23, 3 vols., portr.).

KOVALEVSKAIA, SOFIA VASILEVNA (1850–91). Dynamics.

Sónya Kovalévsky: Her Recollections of Childhood, tr. from the Russian by Isabel F. Hapgood: with a Biography by Anna Carlotta Leffler, Duchess of Cajanello, tr. from the Swedish by A. M. Clive Bayley (New York, 1895: 326 pp., portr.). Both autobiography and biography are excellent. G. Mittag-Leffler, "Weierstrass et Sonja Kowalewsky," in *Acta Mathematica*, vol. 39, pp. 133–198 (1923). A. Borisiak, *Vladimir Onufrievich Kovalevskii* (135 pp., Academy of Sciences, Leningrad, 1928). Biography of Sofia's husband (*Isis*, vol. 12, p. 387).

KRONECKER, LEOPOLD (1823–91). Arithmetization of analysis, theory of functions, elliptic functions.

G. Frobenius, "Gedächtnissrede," in Berlin Akademie der Wissenschaften *Abhandlungen*, 1893. Heinrich Weber, "L. K.," in *Mathematische Annalen*, vol. 43, pp. 1–25 (1893). M. Cantor, in *ADB*, vol. 51, pp. 393–395 (1906). Prasad (1934), pp. 60–93.

Werke, ed. by Kurt Hensel (Leipzig, 1895–1931, 5 vols.). *Vorlesungen über Mathematik* (Leipzig, 1894–1903, 2 vols.).

KUMMER, ERNST EDUARD (1810–93). Theory of numbers, ideal numbers.

Emil Lampe, "Nachruf für E. E. K.," in Deutsche Mathematiker-Vereinigung, *Jahresbericht*, vol. 3, pp. 13–28 (1894). M.

Cantor, in *ADB*, vol. 51, pp. 438–440 (1906). Bernhard Meth, *Zur Erinnerung an E. E. K. als Lehrer* (Berlin, 1910: 20 pp.). Berliner mathematische Gesellschaft, *Festschrift zur Feier des 100. Geburtstages E. K. mit Briefen an seine Mutter und an Leopold Kronecker* (*Abhandlungen zur Geschichte der mathematischen Wissenschaften*, Heft 29, 1910: 103 pp.). Includes biography by Kurt Hensel and portrait.

LAGUERRE, EDMOND (1834–86). Geometrical transformations, numerical equations, theory of functions.

H. Poincaré, *Notice sur Laguerre* (Paris, 1887: 14 pp.)

Oeuvres, ed. by Charles Hermite, H. Poincaré, and E. Rouché (Paris, 1898–1905, 2 vols.).

LAMÉ, GABRIEL (1795–1870). Mathematical physics.

Joseph Bertrand, *Discours prononcé aux funérailles de M. Lamé* (Paris, 1870). Reprinted in Bertrand's *Éloges académiques* (Paris, 1890), pp. 131–158. Léon Sagnet, in *Grande encyclopédie*, vol. 21, pp. 827–828 (1895).

LAPLACE, PIERRE SIMON (1749–1827). Celestial mechanics, probabilities.

Joseph Fourier, *Éloge historique de M. le Mis de Laplace* (Paris, 1829: 22 pp.). François Arago, "Laplace," in his *Oeuvres complètes*, vol. 3, pp. 456–545 (1855). English translation by Baden Powell in *Biographies of Distinguished Scientific Men*, pp. 196–241, reprinted in Smithsonian Institution, *Annual Report*, 1874, pp. 129–168. Henri Andoyer, *L'oeuvre scientifique de Laplace* (Paris, 1922: 162 pp.); cf. *Isis*, vol. 5, pp. 159–160. Émile Picard, *Éloges et discours* (1931), pp. 167–206; cf. *Isis*, vol. 11, p. 393.

Oeuvres (Paris, 1843–47, 7 vols.). *Oeuvres complètes* (Paris, 1878–1912, 14 vols. in 15). Does not include correspondence and biography.

LEGENDRE, ADRIEN MARIE (1752–1833). Theory of numbers, elliptic functions, least squares, elementary geometry.

Éloge historique de A.-M. L., by Léonce Élie de Beaumont, read at the Académie des Sciences in 1861. Englished as "Memoir of Legendre" in Smithsonian Institution, *Annual Report*, 1867, pp. 131–157. Niels Nielsen, *Géomètres français sous la Révolution* (Copenhagen, 1929, pp. 166–174). C. D. Hellman, "Legendre and the French Reform of Weights and Measures," in *Osiris*, vol. 1, pp. 314–340, 2 facs. (1936).

"Correspondance mathématique entre Legendre et Jacobi," in *Journal für die reine und angewandte Mathematik*, vol. 80, pp. 205–279 (1875).

LEJEUNE-DIRICHLET, see DIRICHLET.

LEMOINE, ÉMILE (1840–1912). New triangle geometry, 'geometrography.'

A. Laisant, in *Grande encyclopédie*, vol. 21, p. 1197 (1895).

LEVERRIER, URBAIN JEAN JOSEPH (1811–77). Celestial mechanics.

B. Quaranta, *Monumentum Urbani Leverrier* (Paris, 1846). Charles Emmanuel, *Religion et tolérance de Le V.* (Paris, 1865). Barthélemy Aoust, *Le V., sa vie et ses travaux* (Marseille, 1877). Joseph Bertrand, *Éloge historique de Le V.* (Paris, 1879; reprinted in *Éloges* (1890), pp. 159–192). F. Tisserand, "Travaux de L. V.," in *Annales de l'observatoire*, vol. 15 (Paris, 1880). Louis Brault, "Le V. météorologiste," in *Revue scientifique*, vol. 25, pp. 944–948 (1880). Académie des Sciences, *Centenaire de la naissance de U. J. J. Le V.* (Paris, 1911: 128 pp., 5 pl., facs.).

LIE, SOPHUS (1842–99). Groups of transformation, differential equations.

Felix Klein, *Lectures on Mathematics* (New York, 1894), pp. 9–24. Friedrich Engel, "S. L.," in Sächsische Gesellschaft der Wissenschaften, *Berichte*, math.-phys. Classe, vol. 51, pp. xi–lxi (1899); "S. L.," in Deutsche Mathematiker-Vereinigung, *Jahresbericht*, vol. 8, pp. 30–46 (1900); "S. L.: Ausführliches Verzeichnis seiner Schriften," in *Bibliotheca Mathematica*, 3d series, vol. 1, pp. 166–204, portr. (1900). M. Noether, "S. L.," in *Mathematische Annalen*, vol. 53, pp. 1–41 (1900). M. Cantor, in *ADB*, vol. 51, pp. 695–698 (1906). Alf Guldberg, "Verzeichnis über den wissenschaftlichen Nachlass von S. L.," in Danske Videnskabernes Selskab, *Skrifter*, nat. og math. Afdeling, 1913, no. 5 (44 pp.).

Gesammelte Abhandlungen, ed. by Friedrich Engel and Poul Heegaard (Leipzig, 1922–35, 6 vols.). I have seen vol. 1 in 2 parts, 1934; vol. 2, pt. 1, 1935; vol. 3, 1922; vol. 4 in 2 parts, 1929; vol. 5, 1924; vol. 6 in 2 parts, 1927.

LIOUVILLE, JOSEPH (1809–82). Integration of differential equations, theory of numbers, pure geometry.

Léon Sagnet, in *Grande encyclopédie*, vol. 22, p. 305 (1896).
"Correspondance entre Liouville et Dirichlet," see above, under Dirichlet.

LOBACHEVSKII, NIKOLAI IVANOVICH (1793–1856). Non-Euclidean geometry.

Aleksandr Vasilevich Vasilev, *N. I. L. Address Pronounced at the Commemorative Meeting of the University of Kasan, Oct. 22, 1893*, translated by George Bruce Halsted (Austin, Texas, 1894: 48 pp.). French translation by Mlle. A. Fichtenholtz (Paris, 1896). *Ad Annum MCMXXVI Centesimum a Geometra Kazaniensi N. I. Lobacewski Noneuklideae Geometriae Systematis inventi concelebrandum* (Kazan, 1927: 110 pp.). *N. I. L. In Memoriam*, vol. 2 (Kazan, 1927: 202 pp.).
Collection complète des oeuvres géométriques en russe et en français (Kasan, 1883–86, 2 vols.). *Geometrical Researches on the Theory of Parallels*, translated by G. B. Halsted (Austin, Texas, 1891; new ed., with portrait and bibliography, Chicago, 1914).

LORENTZ, HENDRIK ANTOON (1853–1928). Mathematical physics, relativity.

Recueil de travaux offerts par les auteurs à H. A. Lorentz (*Archives néerlandaises des sciences exactes et naturelles*, 2d series, vol. 5, La Haye, 1900). Ethel Truman, in Encyclopaedia Britannica, 14th ed., vol. 14, p. 393 (1929).
Collected Papers, vols. 1 (with portr.), 7, 8 (The Hague, 1935, '34–'35). *Abhandlungen über theoretische Physik*, vol. 1 (Leipzig, 1907: 490 pp.). No more published. *Vorlesungen über theoretische Physik* (Leipzig, 1927–31, 5 vols.).

MACCULLAGH, JAMES (1809–47). Analytic geometry, quadrics, attraction of ellipsoids, wave theory.

Charles Platts, in *DNB*, vol. 35, p. 15 (1893).
Collected works, ed. by John Hewitt Jellett and Samuel Haughton (Dublin, 1880: 390 pp.).

MAXWELL, JAMES CLERK (1831–79). Mathematical physics, electromagnetic theory.

Lewis Campbell and William Garnett, *The Life of J. C. M.* (London, 1882, 678 pp., 3 portr.; new ed., abridged and revised, London, 1884, 436 pp.). Sir Richard Tetley Glazebrook, *J. C. M. and Modern Physics* (New York, 1896: 224 pp.). *A Commemoration Volume, J. C. M. 1831–1931* (Cambridge, 1931: 152 pp., portr.); cf. *Isis*, vol. 21, p. 400.

Scientific Papers, ed. by Sir William Davidson Niven (Cambridge, 1890, 2 vols.; photographic reprint, 1927). Includes a brief biographical sketch and a portrait.

MÉRAY, CHARLES (1835–1911). Theory of irrationals.

Joseph Pionchon, "Notice sur la vie et les travaux de C. M.," in *Revue bourguignonne*, vol. 22, pp. 1–158 (Dijon, 1912).

MINKOWSKI, HERMANN (1864–1909). Relativity, mathematical physics.

David Hilbert, "H. M.: Gedächtnisrede," in Göttingen Gesellschaft der Wissenschaften, *Nachrichten*, Geschäftliche Mitteilungen, 1909, pp. 72–101.

Gesammelte Abhandlungen, ed. by David Hilbert (Leipzig, 1911, 2 vols.).

MITTAG-LEFFLER, GÖSTA (1846–1927). Theory of functions.

Prasad (1934), pp. 212–244, portr.

For the Mittag-Leffler Institute, see above at the end of the Bibliography, Section VIII, D.

MÖBIUS, AUGUST FERDINAND (1790–1868). Barycentrical calculus.

Heinrich Gretschel, "A. F. M.," in *Archiv der Mathematik und Physik*, vol. 49, Literarischer Bericht clxxxxv, pp. 1–9 (1869). M. Cantor, in *ADB*, vol. 22, pp. 38–43 (1885).

Gesammelte Werke (Leipzig, 1885–87, 4 vols.). There is a short biographical sketch by R. Baltzer in vol. 1.

NEUMANN, FRANZ (1798–1895). Spherical functions, mathematical physics, crystallography.

Paul Volkmann, *F. N.* (Leipzig, 1896: 74 pp., portr.). Luise Neumann, *F. N.: Erinnerungsblätter von seiner Tochter* (Tübingen,

1904: 475 pp., portr.). Robert Knott, in *ADB*, vol. 52, pp. 680–684 (1906). Albert Wangerin, *F. N. und sein Wirken als Forscher und Lehrer* (Braunschweig, 1907: 195 pp., portr.).

Gesammelte Werke (Leipzig, 1906–28, 3 vols.). *Vorlesungen über mathematische Physik* (Leipzig, 1881–94, 7 vols.).

NEWCOMB, SIMON (1835–1909).   Celestial mechanics.

The Reminiscences of an Astronomer (Boston, 1903: 434 pp., portr.). An autobiography.

"S. N.: Memorial Addresses," in *Bulletin* of the Philosophical Society of Washington, vol. 15, pp. 133–167 (1910). W. W. Campbell and Raymond Clare Archibald, "S. N.," in National Academy of Sciences, *Memoirs*, vol. 17, first memoir (Washington, 1924). Charles G. Abbott, in *DAB*, vol. 13, pp. 452–455 (1934).

Newcomb's manuscripts and letters are preserved in the Library of Congress.

NOETHER, EMMY (1882–1935).   Theory of ideals, non-commutative algebras.

Obituary by A. Einstein in the *New York Times*, May 4, 1935, and by Hermann Weyl in *Scripta Mathematica*, vol. 3, pp. 201–220 (1935), with portrait.

OLBERS, WILHELM (1758–1840).   Celestial mechanics.

Wilhelm Olbers Focke, "Heinrich Wilhelm Matthias Olbers," in *Bremische Biographie* (Bremen, 1912), pp. 359–376.

W. O., sein Leben und seine Werke, ed. by Carl Schilling (2 vols. in 3, Berlin, 1894–09, with portr.; supplement, 1899).

Briefwechsel zwischen W. O. und F. W. Bessel, see above, under Bessel.

OPPOLZER, THEODOR VON (1841–86).   Celestial mechanics.

Siegmund Günther, in *ADB*, vol. 52, pp. 710–712 (1906).

PAINLEVÉ, PAUL (1863–1933).   Differential equations, mechanics.

Obituary notices by Émile Borel and Émile Picard, in Académie des Sciences, *Comptes rendus*, vol. 197, pp. 953–958 (1933). Short notice in *Revue scientifique*, vol. 71, pp. 669–670 (1933). Notices by Victor Basch, Paul Langevin, and Fernand Bouisson, in *Les cahiers des droits de l'homme*, vol. 33, pp. 651–655 (1933).

"P. L.," in *Les cahiers rationalistes*, no. 26, pp. 230–260 (1933). Germaine André Hesse, *P., grand savant, grand citoyen* (Paris, 1933: 246 pp.).

PEACOCK, GEORGE (1791–1858). Foundations of algebra.

J. Willis Clark, in *DNB*, vol. 44, pp. 138–140 (1895). Macfarlane, *British Mathematicians*, pp. 7–18.

PEIRCE, BENJAMIN (1809–80). Linear associative algebra.

R. C. Archibald, *B. P., 1809–1880* (Oberlin, 1925: 34 pp.). The same, in *DAB*, vol. 14, pp. 393–397 (1934).

A considerable quantity of Peirce's manuscripts and correspondence is preserved in the archives of the American Academy of Arts and Sciences in Boston.

PFAFF, JOHANN FRIEDRICH (1765–1825). Differential equations.

Moritz Cantor, in *ADB*, vol. 25, pp. 592–593 (1887).

PLÜCKER, JULIUS (1801–68). Analytic and infinitesimal geometry, analytic formulation of the principle of duality, foundation of modern analytic geometry.

Adolf Dronke, *J. P.* (Bonn, 1871: 31 pp.). Alfred Clebsch, "Zum Gedächniss an J. P.," in Göttingen Gesellschaft der Wissenschaften, *Abhandlungen*, vol. 16, Math. Classe (1871: 40 pp.). French translation, with additions by P. Mansion, in *Bullettino di bibliografia e di storia delle scienze matematiche e fisiche*, vol. 5, pp. 183–212 (1872). Gustav Karsten, in *ADB*, vol. 26, pp. 321–323 (1888). Wilhelm Ernst, *J. P.* (Bonn, 1933: 90 pp.).

Gesammelte wissenschaftliche Abhandlungen, ed. by Arthur Schoenflies and Friedrich Pockels (Leipzig, 1895–96, 2 vols.). The memoir by Alfred Clebsch is included in vol. 1.

POINCARÉ, HENRI (1854–1912). Theory of functions, Fuchsian and Abelian functions, differential equations, celestial mechanics, mathematical physics, philosophy of science.

Ernest Lebon, *H. P.* (Paris, 1909, 88 pp., portr.; 2d ed., 1912, 115 pp.). Édouard Toulouse, *H. P.* (Paris, 1910: 204 pp.). Robert d'Adhémar, *H. P.* (Paris, 1912, 41 pp.; 2d ed., 1914, 64 pp.). George Sarton, "H. P.," in *Ciel et terre; Bulletin de la Société belge d'astronomie* (1913: 25 pp., portr.). Includes intimate details not found elsewhere. Émile Picard, "L'oeuvre de H. P.," in École Normale Supérieure, *Annales scientifiques*, 3ᵉ série, vol. 30, pp. 463–482 (1913). Reprinted in his *Discours et mélanges* (1922), pp. 201–220; see also his *Éloges et discours* (1931), pp. 289–296. Articles by L. Brunschvicg, J. Hadamard, A. Lebeuf, and P. Langevin, in *Revue de métaphysique et de morale*, vol. 21, pp. 585–718 (1913). Gaston Darboux, "Éloge historique d'H. P.," in Académie des Sciences, *Mémoires*, vol. 52, pp. lxxxi–cxlviii, portr. (1914). Vito Volterra, Jacques Hadamard, Paul Langevin, Pierre Boutroux, *H. P.* (Paris, 1914: 270 pp.). Louis Rougier, *La philosophie géométrique de H. P.* (Paris, 1920: 208 pp.). Paul Appell, *H. P.* (Paris, 1925: 120 pp., portr.). Prasad (1934), pp. 278–321. See also *Isis*, vol. 1, pp. 172, 311; vol. 4, p. 169; vol. 5, p. 256.

Poincaré's *Oeuvres* are in course of publication, ten volumes being planned. Vol. 2, including Darboux's *Éloge historique*, appeared in Paris, 1916. Vol. 1, ed. by Paul Appell and Jules Drach, appeared in 1928; vol. 3, ed. by Drach, in 1934. "Correspondance de H. P. et de Felix Klein," ed. by N. E. Nörlund, in Acta Mathematica, vol. 39, pp. 94–132 (1923).

POINSOT, LOUIS (1777–1859). Statics and dynamics.

Joseph Bertrand, *Éloges académiques*, nouvelle série, pp. 1–27.

POISSON, DENIS (1781–1840). Mechanics, mathematical physics, celestial mechanics, probabilities.

Discours by Arago, read in 1850. Charles Hermite, in *Bulletin des sciences mathématiques*, deuxième série, vol. 14, pp. 9–14 (1890).

PONCELET, JEAN VICTOR (1788–1867). Projective geometry.

Isidore Didion, *Notice sur la vie et les ouvrages du général J.-V. P.* (Paris, 1869: 59 pp.). Elling Bolt Holst, *Om P.'s Betydning for Geometrien* (Christiania, 1878: 162 pp.). J. Bertrand, "Éloge historique de J.-V. P.," in Académie des Sciences, *Mémoires*, vol. 41, pt. 2, pp. i–xxv (1879), and *Éloges académiques* (1890), pp. 105–129.

RAMANUJAN, SRINIVASA (1887–1920). Theory of numbers.

Collected Papers, ed. by G. H. Hardy, P. V. Seshu Aiyar, and B. M. Wilson (Cambridge, 1927: 392 pp.). With biography and portrait.

RANKINE, WILLIAM JOHN MACQUORN (1820–72). Thermodynamics, molecular physics.

G. C. Boase, in *DNB*, vol. 47, pp. 290–292 (1896). Macfarlane, *British Physicists*, pp. 22–37. Sir James Blacklock Henderson, *M. R.* (Glasgow, 1932: 28 pp.).
Miscellaneous Scientific Papers, ed. by William J. Millar (London, 1881: 603 pp., portr.). With a memoir by P. G. Tait.

RAYLEIGH, LORD (JOHN WILLIAM STRUTT, THIRD BARON RAYLEIGH) (1842–1919). Mathematical physics, chiefly acoustics.

Robert John Strutt (the present, fourth, Baron Rayleigh), *The Life of J. W. S., Third Baron Rayleigh* (London, 1924); cf. *Isis*, vol. 8, pp. 177–181.
Scientific Papers (Cambridge, 1899–1920, 6 vols.).

RIEMANN, BERNHARD (1826–66). Differential and integral equations, principles of geometry, non-Euclidean geometry.

Heinrich Burkhardt, *B. R.* (Göttingen, 1892: 12 pp.). Felix Klein, *R. und seine Bedeutung für die Entwicklung der modernen Mathematik* (Leipzig, 1894: 18 pp.). Prasad (1933), pp. 291–344.
Gesammelte mathematische Werke und wissenschaftlicher Nachlass, ed. by Heinrich Weber (1st ed., 1876; 2d ed., Leipzig, 1892, 568 pp., portr.). With a biography by Richard Dedekind. *Nachträge*, ed. by M. Noether and W. Wirtinger (Leipzig, 1902: 124 pp.). French translation of the greatest part by L. Laugel (Paris, 1898: 488 pp.).

ROSENHAIN, JOHANN GEORG (1816–87). Double theta functions.

M. Cantor, in *ADB*, vol. 29, p. 209 (1889).

RUFFINI, PAOLO (1765–1822). Theory of equations.

Heinrich Burkhardt, "Die Anfänge der Gruppentheorie und P. R.," in *Abhandlungen zur Geschichte der mathematischen Wissenschaften*, Heft 6, pp. 119–159 (1892). E. Bortolotti, *Influenza dell'opera matematica di P. R.* (Modena, 1902: 57 pp.).
Opere matematiche, ed. by Ettore Bortolotti (Palermo, 1915–).
"Carteggio di P. R. con alcuni scienziati del suo tempo," ed. by Ettore Bortolotti, in Società Italiana delle Scienze, *Memorie*, 3 serie, vol. 14, pp. 291–325 (1906).

SAINT-VENANT, ADHÉMAR BARRÉ, COMTE DE (1797–1886). Theory of elasticity, vectorial analysis, hydrodynamics.

Isaac Todhunter (1820–84), *A History of the Theory of Elasticity and of the Strength of Materials*, ed. and completed by Karl Pearson (Cambridge, 1886–93, 2 vols.). Vol. 1, Galilei to Saint-Venant, 1639–1850; vol. 2, Saint-Venant to Lord Kelvin.

SCHWARZ, HERMANN AMANDUS (1843–1921). Conform representation of surfaces, minimal surfaces.

Mathematische Abhandlungen H. A. S. zu seinem fünfzigjährigen Doktorjubiläum gewidmet (Berlin, 1914: 460 pp., portr.). Constantin Carathéodory, in *Deutsches biographisches Jahrbuch*, vol. 3, pp. 236–238 (1927).

Gesammelte mathematische Abhandlungen (Berlin, 1890, 2 vols.).

SMITH, HENRY JOHN STEPHEN (1826–83). Theory of numbers.

J. W. L. Glaisher, in Royal Astronomical Society, *Monthly Notices*, vol. 44 (1884). A. M. Clerke, in *DNB*, vol. 53, pp. 50–53 (1898). Macfarlane, *British Mathematicians*, pp. 92–106.

Collected Mathematical Papers, ed. by J. W. L. Glaisher (Oxford, 1894, 2 vols.). With biographical sketches and a portrait.

STAUDT, KARL GEORG CHRISTIAN VON (1798–1867). Synthetic geometry, *Geometrie der Lage*, geometric interpretation of imaginary elements.

Carl Friedrich Philipp von Martius, "C. G. C. von Staudt," in *Archiv der Mathematik und Physik*, vol. 49, Literarischer Bericht clxxxxiii, pp. 1–5 (1869). M. Cantor, in *ADB*, vol. 35, p. 520 (1893). Max Noether," Zur Erinnerung an K. G. C. von S.," in University of Erlangen, *Festschrift dem Prinzregenten Luitpold dargebracht* (Erlangen, 1901), vol. 4, pt. 2, pp. 63–86.

STEINER, JACOB (1796–1863). Synthetic geometry.

Otto Hesse, "J. S.," in *Journal für die reine und angewandte Mathematik*, vol. 62, pp. 199–200 (1863). C. F. Geiser, *Zur Erinnerung an J. S.* (Schaffhausen, 1874: 37 pp.). M. Cantor, in *ADB*, vol. 35, pp. 700–703 (1893). Johann Heinrich Graf, *Der Mathematiker J. S. von Utzenstorf* (Bern, 1897: 54 pp., portr.). Julius Lange, *Jacob Steiners Lebensjahre in Berlin, 1821–1863, nach seinen Personalakten dargestellt* (Berlin, 1899: 70 pp., portr.). Emil Lampe, "Zur Biographie von J. S.," in *Bibliotheca Mathematica*, 3d series, vol. 1, pp. 129–141 (1900).

Gesammelte Werke, ed. by Karl Weierstrass (Berlin, 1881–82, 2 vols.).

"Briefwechsel zwischen J. S. und L. Schläfli" (208 pp.), ed. by J. H. Graf, in Naturforschende Gesellschaft, Bern, *Mittheilungen* (1896).

STOKES, SIR GEORGE GABRIEL (1819–1903). Mathematical physics.

Sir Joseph Larmor, in *DNB*, 2d sup., vol. 3, pp. 421–424 (1912). Macfarlane, *British Physicists*, pp. 94–105.

Mathematical and Physical Papers (Cambridge, 1880–1905, 5 vols.). Includes obituary by Lord Rayleigh in vol. 5 and portraits. *Memoir and Scientific Correspondence*, ed. by Sir Joseph Larmor (Cambridge, 1907, 2 vols.). Biographical notes and appreciations by various hands, portraits.

SYLOW, LUDVIG (1832–1918). Substitution groups.

Helge Bergh Kragemo, *Ludvig Sylow* (Oslo, 1933, in Norwegian: 27 pp.).

Skrifter (1933), including biography, bibliography, portrait.

SYLVESTER, JAMES JOSEPH (1814–97). Invariants, theory of equations, theory of numbers, multiple algebra.

Fabian Franklin, *An Address Commemorative of J. J. S.* (Baltimore, 1897: 15 pp.). P. A. MacMahon, in Royal Society of London, *Proceedings*, vol. 63, pp. ix–xxv, with portr. (1898). P. E. Matheson and E. B. Elliott, in *DNB*, vol. 55, pp. 258–260 (1898). Macfarlane, *British Mathematicians*, pp. 107–121. David S. Blondheim, *A Brilliant and Eccentric Mathematician* (Baltimore, 1921: 22 pp.). Émile Picard, *Mélanges de mathématiques et de physique*, pp. 29–34 (1924). R. C. Archibald, "Unpublished Letters of J. J. S. and other New Information concerning his Life and Work," in *Osiris* 1, pp. 85–154 (1936). D. E. Smith, in *DAB*, vol. 18, pp. 256–257 (1936).

Collected Mathematical Papers, ed. by H. F. Baker (Cambridge, 1904–12, 4 vols.). With biographical notice and portrait in vol. 4.

TAIT, PETER GUTHRIE (1831–1901). Mechanics, mathematical physics, quaternions.

Alexander Macfarlane, "P. G. T.," in *Bibliotheca Mathematica*, 3d series, vol. 4, pp. 185–200, portr. (1903). Cargill Gilston Knott, *Life and Scientific Work of P. G. T.* (Cambridge, 1911: 388 pp., 4 portr.). J. H. Hamilton Dickson, in *DNB*, 2d supp., vol. 3, pp. 471–474 (1912). Macfarlane, *British Physicists*, pp. 38–54.

Scientific Papers (Cambridge, 1898–1900, 2 vols.). *Lectures on some Recent Advances in Physical Science* (London, 1876: 350 pp.).

TCHEBYCHEV, see CHEBYSHEV.

THOMSON, SIR WILLIAM, see KELVIN.

WEIERSTRASS, KARL (1815–97). Theory of functions.

Wilhelm Killing, *K. W.* (Münster i. W., 1897: 21 pp.). Emil Lampe, *K. W.* (Leipzig, 1897: 24 pp.). Karl von Voit, "Karl Theodor Wilhelm W.," in Munich Akademie der Wissenschaften, *Sitzungsberichte*, math.-phys. Classe, vol. 27, pp. 402–409 (1897). H. Poincaré, "L'oeuvre mathématique de W.," in *Acta Mathematica*, vol. 22, pp. 1–18 (1898); *Savants et écrivains* (1910), pp. 201–212. G. Mittag-Leffler, "W.," in *Acta Mathematica*, vol. 21, pp. 79–82 (1897); "Zur Biographie von W.," *ibidem*, vol. 35, pp. 29–65 (1911); "Die ersten 40 Jahre des Lebens von W.," *ibidem*, vol. 39, pp. 1–57 (1923). Émile Picard, *Mélanges de mathématiques et physique* (1924), pp. 23–28. Prasad (1933), pp. 220–290.

Mathematische Werke (Berlin, 1894–1927, 7 vols.). Portrait in vol. 3.

It would be interesting to name these 118 mathematicians in chronological order. A rough way of doing this is to name them in order of their death years; their main activities may not have occurred exactly in the same order, but at any rate the death year is a superior limit of the activity of each person.

1822	Ruffini	1867	Poncelet
1823	L. Carnot		Staudt
1825	Pfaff	1868	Möbius
1827	Fresnel		Plücker
	Laplace	1870	Lamé
1829	Abel	1871	Babbage
1830	Fourier		De Morgan
1831	Germain	1872	Clebsch
1832	Galois		Rankine
1833	Legendre	1874	Hesse
1840	Olbers	1877	Cournot
	Poisson		Grassmann
1841	Green		Leverrier
1842	Ivory	1879	Clifford
1846	Bessel		Maxwell
1847	Göpel	1880	Bellavitis
	MacCullagh		Chasles
1848	Bolzano		Borchardt
1851	Jacobi		B. Peirce
1852	Eisenstein	1882	Jevons
1855	Gauss		Liouville
1856	F. Bólyai	1883	H. J. S. Smith
	Lobachevskii	1884	Aronhold
1857	Cauchy	1886	Laguerre
1858	Peacock		Oppolzer
1859	Dirichlet		Saint-Venant
	Poinsot	1887	Kirchhoff
1860	J. Bólyai		Rosenhain
1863	Steiner	1888	Clausius
1864	Boole	1889	Halphen
1865	Encke	1891	Kovalevskaia
	Hamilton		Kronecker
1866	Riemann		

1892	Adams	1912	Darwin
	Airy		Fiedler
	Betti		Gordan
1893	Kummer		Lemoine
1894	Chebyshev		Poincaré
	Helmholtz	1913	Ball
	Hertz	1914	Couturat
1895	Cayley		Hill
	Neumann	1916	Dedekind
1897	Brioschi	1917	Darboux
	Sylvester	1918	Georg Cantor
	Weierstrass		Sylow
1899	Lie	1919	Rayleigh
1900	Beltrami	1920	Bachmann
	Bertrand		Ramanujan
1901	Hermite	1921	Schwarz
	Tait	1922	Jordan
1902	Fuchs	1925	Frege
1903	Cremona		Klein
	Gibbs	1926	Edgeworth
	Stokes	1927	Fredholm
1906	Boltzmann		Mittag-Leffler
1907	Kelvin	1928	Lorentz
1909	Minkowski	1930	Appell
	Newcomb	1932	Baire
1911	Méray	1933	Painlevé
		1935	E. Noether

I do not assert that these 118 men are the most important
mathematicians of modern times. Such a statement would be
very foolish. All of them are important, though in very different
ways. A few men, like Gauss, tower above all their contemporaries
like giants, but with regard to the other distinguished mathematicians it is impossible to determine their relative rank, as this
would imply quantitative measurements of mathematical genius
which are quite inconceivable. As I have examined every field
of mathematics without prejudice, and I have a good deal of experience, it is probable that my selection is fairly representative;
it may serve as a first approximation.

Any competent person glancing through my list will become more fully aware of the almost incredible richness and complexity of modern mathematics. One may object that I have increased that complexity by including a number of physicists and astronomers who did a good deal of mathematical work but were not pure mathematicians. I did it because it is essential that mathematicians should be made to realize the fundamental importance (even from their point of view) of applied mathematics. This should be the first great lesson of the history of mathematics. There are many currents of influence connecting the various branches of pure mathematics with the various branches of applied mathematics; each current may flow in either direction; it may be interrupted for a time, but many of them are always flowing in one way or another, and no interruption should be considered final. Every mathematician is influenced by some of these currents, whether he realizes it or not, but it is better for him to realize it, and to trace each influence to its very source.

Mathematical students interested in the history of their subject would do well to begin with reading a few biographies. They would naturally select the biographies of the mathematicians in whom they are most interested and whom they have learned to know and to admire above all others. My list may help them in this, but if they try to use it, they may be disappointed. Indeed the number of full-size biographies is relatively small. We have biographies of Abel, Bólyai, Lobachevskii, Cauchy, De Morgan, Hamilton, Jevons, Kelvin, Maxwell, Rayleigh, Tait, Encke, Grassmann, Helmholtz, Jacobi, Olbers; and to these might be added a few autobiographies, by Cournot, Appell, Airy, Babbage, Ball, Newcomb, and Sofia Kovalevskaia. That is not very much. The list of mathematicians whose life has never been told with any detail is considerably longer. Moreover, these few full-length biographies are not always all that they should be. Cauchy's, for example, is very insufficient.

This may be disappointing, but it is also stimulating, for it reveals once more the immensity of the work remaining to be done. Think that we are still lacking a satisfactory biography of Gauss, one of the greatest heroes of mankind! And yet there is no lack of documents, but on the contrary an abundance of them. In addition to his works, we have no less than eleven volumes of letters, many of them addressed to other mathematicians (Schumacher, Nicolai, Bessel, Bólyai, Olbers, Gerling) to whom he confided his perplexities and with whom he discussed his problems. Moreover, under Klein's direction there has been published a series of preliminary studies, each of which explains the development of Gauss's thought in a particular field: theory of numbers, theory of functions, geometry, astronomy, algebra, etc. It does not follow that a biography of that giant would be easy to compose, far from it; the task, in itself considerable, would be increased by the very abundance of materials; it would imply a life of devotion. If men have spent a lifetime studying Bach or Beethoven, would a lifetime devoted to Gauss be ill spent? What is there greater in nature than a great man? Is not a great scientist quite as interesting as a great artist or a famous soldier? And, to ask one more question, why is the study of savage psychology deemed to be a proper scientific subject, and the study of genius a sort of dilettantism?

To take another example, consider Poincaré. In addition to his voluminous mathematical books and memoirs, he wrote many articles wherein he revealed his heart and mind more completely than most mathematicians. Moreover we owe to Dr. Édouard Toulouse (1910) a study which is almost unique in the whole gamut of biography. He investigated Poincaré's heredity, and submitted him to a number of 'medico-psychological' tests. Thus here again the ingredients of a great biography exist, but the biography itself is still unwritten.

The intelligent reading of the life of a mathematician would naturally lead to his works. Students may thus be induced to attack one of his treatises, or to examine a whole series of his papers. For this purpose my list will be useful, as it will tell them quickly whether 'collected works' are available or not. The existence of 'collected works' makes the study of the evolution of a man's thought much easier; without them one is obliged to refer to odd volumes of a number of periodicals, a process very tiresome at best, and for those out of reach of a large library almost impossible.[1]

[1] It should be noted that the editors of collected works are obliged first of all to prepare a bibliography of all the writings; when the works have not been collected, that bibliography itself is generally lacking, and the finding

A copy of Laplace's works is given to the ranking student of each promotion of the École Polytechnique. A princely gift indeed, and one well calculated to rouse and inflame a zeal for mathematics, and perhaps also for the history of the subject.[1] Few students can afford to buy a set of Laplace's works, but many other sets of collected works, being much smaller, can be obtained at reasonable prices and constitute an incomparable possession. A student owning a good biography and the collected works of a mathematician can begin and continue at leisure a deep study of his thought and fate. The reading of monographs will give him a more intimate contact with the realities and creative processes of mathematics than almost any textbook. The work may be hard, for many mathematicians have a tendency to conceal their own methods of discovery, to take all the scaffolding away, and present their results in the most synthetic and unapproachable manner; but in such cases the efforts made to understand the subject will imply a recreation of it, and this will be at one and the same time the best of mathematical exercises and the best way of penetrating the mathematician's thought far below the surface.

---

of the works and papers is a difficult task. An additional practical difficulty is due to the fact that many libraries refuse to lend early volumes of periodicals for outside use. They cannot be blamed for this, for the loss of a single volume destroys the integrity of the whole set.

[1] The award is made by the Académie des Sciences, a special foundation for that purpose having been endowed by Laplace's widow in 1836. See Pierre Gauja, *Les fondations de l'Académie des Sciences* (Hendaye, 1917), pp. 131–134. I am indebted for this information to Général Hachette, commandant of the École Polytechnique (kind letter of December 2, 1935).

INDEX

INDEX I

INDEX II

THE STUDY OF THE HISTORY
OF SCIENCE

by

George Sarton

DOVER PUBLICATIONS, INC.

NEW YORK

CONTENTS

THE STUDY OF THE HISTORY
OF SCIENCE

THE STUDY OF THE HISTORY OF SCIENCE

THE publication of university lectures may not, in general, be desirable, because it is better that they be kept in as fluid a state as possible, but an exception should be made for inaugural lectures. Indeed, each of these lectures is, or should be, a milestone, and the examination of several of them relating to a single discipline enables us to measure the progress of that subject in a manner doubly pleasant, because concrete and informal. As it is my privilege to inaugurate, not only this seminary, but also the scientific study of the history of science in Harvard University, I feel it to be a part of my duty to explain my task as I understand it. I hope that in so doing I am beginning a new tradition, and that my successors will take pains to explain the same task, as they understand it, when it shall be their privilege in the course of time to assume it.

One might assert that there is nothing new in the history of science, because it is simply the application of the well known methods of history to the well known facts of science. This is specious. The elements of our discipline may be as old as you please, their combination is relatively new. It is true some historical efforts were made as early as the fourth century B.C. by Aristotle's pupil, Eudemos of Rhodes, and these efforts were continued by other Greeks; furthermore there has come down to us from the Middle Ages and modern times a whole series of writings in Arabic, Latin, and other languages, which might be catalogued under the heading 'history of science.' Nevertheless, the first scholar to conceive that subject as an independent discipline and to realize its importance was the French philosopher Auguste Comte (1798–1857), and the scholar who deserves perhaps more than any other to be called the father of our studies,

Paul Tannery (1843–1904), could write, as late as 1904, "To-day this history [i. e., the history of science] is nothing but an individual conception." [1] What Tannery meant was that that history was not yet represented by an array of noble books constituting the tradition of a definite kind of scholarship different from all others. One wonders whether he was acquainted with Whewell's work. The chances are he was not.[2] In any case Whewell's conception of the history of science was still primitive and somewhat narrow, and his realization of it imperfect. Postponing the discussion of his priority, it is clear that the history of science is a relatively new discipline. Whether it be fifty years old, or a hundred, it is still so young that I should not hesitate to repeat Tannery's statement. It is not yet crystallized in the sense that the 'history of England' is, or even the 'history of religion.' Not to speak of an 'array' of books, there is not yet a single one which is so good that one can refer to it to the exclusion of others, not yet a single one which is truly worthy of the subject. We are still turning around it, approaching and investing it from every side; we do not yet master it.

* * *

In fact, most scholars misunderstand its true nature. This is not surprising, in view of its dual origin. Whom shall we consider the best prepared and most expert, him who understands the subject or him who knows the methods? In the *history* of *science* shall we emphasize the first word or the second? It is clear also that our definition of the new discipline will be colored by our conception, or miscon-

---

[1] Paul Tannery, "De l'histoire générale des sciences," *Revue de synthèse historiques*, vol. 8 (1904), p. 7.

[2] William Whewell (1794–1866). His *History of the Inductive Sciences from the Earliest to the Present Times* (1837, 3 vols.) was as little known in the French world as it was well known in the English world. It was soon translated into German (1840–41) but not into French.

ception, of historiography on the one hand and of science on the other, and even by our philosophical beliefs or prejudices.

Before proceeding further, it may be useful to repeat a definition and a theorem which I have published in various forms in earlier writings since 1913.

Definition. Science is systematized positive knowledge, or what has been taken as such at different ages and in different places.

Theorem. The acquisition and systematization of positive knowledge are the only human activities which are truly cumulative and progressive.

Corollary. The history of science is the only history which can illustrate the progress of mankind. In fact, progress has no definite and unquestionable meaning in other fields than the field of science.

To be sure, we should not be dazzled by the shibboleth 'progress,' for there are other features of human life which are at least as precious as scientific activities, though they are unprogressive: charity and the love of beauty, for example. But if we wish to explain the progress of mankind, then we must focus our attention on the development of science and its applications.

Moreover, we shall not be able to understand our own science of to-day (I do not say to use it, but to understand it) if we do not succeed in penetrating its genesis and evolution. Knowledge is not something dead and static, but something fluid, alive, and moving. The latest results are like the new fruits of a tree; the fruits serve our immediate practical purposes, but for all that it is the tree that matters. The scientist of philosophic mind is not interested so much in the latest results of science as he is in its eternal tendencies, in the living and exuberant and immortal tree. The fruits of to-day may be tempting enough, but they are not more precious to his way of thinking than those of yesterday or to-morrow.

One might thus expect the more intelligent scientists to appreciate the historical point of view, but most of them are so busy, so anxious to be always at the very frontier of expanding knowledge, that they have neither inclination nor time to look backward. Even when they are historically-minded, which is seldom the case, they are so keenly aware of their purely scientific difficulties that they are prone by way of contrast to minimize, or to overlook entirely, the historical ones. Having finally reached a summit whence they could dominate the past, either they consider retrospection an unwarranted indulgence and dereliction of duty, or they look backward so clumsily that they cannot see anything with precision. You may remember Littré's earnest words in the first volume of his magnificent edition of Hippocrates:

Quand on s'est pénétré de la science contemporaine, alors il est temps de se tourner vers la science passée. Rien ne fortifie plus le jugement que cette comparison. L'impartialité de l'esprit s'y développe; l'incertitude des systèmes s'y manifeste; l'autorité des faits s'y confirme, et l'on découvre, dans l'ensemble, un enchaînement philosophique qui est en soi une leçon. En d'autres termes, on apprend à connaître, à comprendre, à juger.[1]

"When one has imbued one's self with the scientific knowledge of to-day, *then it is time* to turn toward the science of the past" . . . but the poor devils have no time to study the past, nor have they the faintest idea of how to study it. As the scientific training is enormously more difficult, and requires the unintermitting effort of years and years, indeed, of a lifetime, they are prone to think that it is sufficient. Alas! Indispensable as it is, it is not enough. The historical training is, or may be, much easier than the scientific one, but it is equally necessary.

* * *

The obvious difference between the scientific preparation and the historical one is that the former is not only much

[1] Emile Littré, *Oeuvres complètes d'Hippocrate* (Paris, 1839), vol. 1, p. 477.

longer but more systematic; it must be carried on in a certain order. One cannot study analysis before algebra, nor physiology before chemistry and physics. On the other hand, it is possible, though perhaps unadvisable, to study history in almost any order, and the majority of scholars have obtained their historical knowledge in the most haphazard way. One may be an expert in American history and know nothing whatever of the Sumerians or the Hittites. Some time ago I was obliged to examine the work of a Transylvanian chemist who flourished at the end of the eighteenth century. To appreciate his work it was necessary to consider on the one hand the historical *milieu*, and on the other the contemporary chemical traditions. I knew nothing of the history of Transylvania at that time, but it did not cost me much trouble to obtain the information which I needed, or, with the aid of my knowledge of comparable conditions elsewhere, to understand it. Happily I was well acquainted with chemistry and the chemical knowledge of that period in Western Europe and with the so-called 'chemical revolution,' subjects in which it would have been impossible for me to remedy my ignorance so readily. I should have been obliged to study chemistry and the complete history of chemistry down to that time!

However, the most fundamental difference between historical knowledge and scientific knowledge is revealed by the way they grow. Historical knowledge grows slowly and precariously; precariously, because of the constant recurrence of discredited errors; slowly, because of increasing difficulty in obtaining new material. Though our knowledge tends toward completeness, it is asymptotic, and never reaches the goal. For example, consider our knowledge of ancient Greece. It continues to improve, to be sure, but with smaller and smaller increments of truth. It will not be more difficult, it will probably be simpler, to study it a few centuries hence than now. On the contrary, any branch of science may be completely revolutionized at any time by a

discovery necessitating a radically new approach to the subject. Chemistry to-day is essentially different from chemistry in the eighteenth century. The fundamental notions
are different, the methods are different, the scope is in-
credibly larger, and the contents infinitely more varied.
We may safely assume that the chemistry of the twenty-
fifth century will be as unlike that of the present as that, in
turn, is unlike that of the fifteenth century. On the other
hand, in the twenty-fifth century or in the thirtieth it will
take about the same pains and time as to-day to study Latin
grammar, Greek literature, or the history of the eighteenth
century. The literary subjects, we may say, tend to be
closed subjects, whose expansion after a certain point is so
slow as to be imperceptible. In strong contrast with them,
the growth of scientific subjects is unpredictable, luxuriant,
and sometimes explosive in its intensity and destructiveness.

The scientist, then, can never relax in his efforts and
enjoy himself, like a genial and sensible grammarian, but
must be prepared to learn new things every day, and, what
is worse, unlearn others with which he has grown intimate,
and change the tenets of a life time on fundamental points.
No wonder that such a harassed individual is generally un-
willing to contemplate the past, or, should he have any
velleities to do so, unable to do it well. He innocently believes, it may be, that he knows how to do it. Historical
work, he seems to think, consists in taking a few old books
and copying from them this and that. He may be well
trained and fastidious in his own exacting technique, yet not
realize that the technique of establishing the truth, or the
maximum probability, of past events has its own complicated rules and methods. Historical work, as he conceives it
in his candor, is exceedingly easy; almost all that is needed,
he thinks, is to know how to read and write, and he despises
it accordingly. He does not realize that he is merely despis-
ing his perverted image of it. The historian whom he
scorns and ridicules is nobody but himself.

⁎

The difference between the historical and the scientific points of view has been amusingly illustrated by Henri Poincaré as follows: [1]

> Carlyle has written somewhere something like this: "Nothing but facts are of importance. John Lackland passed by here. Here is something that is admirable. Here is a reality for which I would give all the theories in the world." Carlyle was a countryman of Bacon . . ., but Bacon would not have said that. That is the language of the historian. The physicist would say rather: "John Lackland passed by here; I don't care, for he will not pass this way again."

Physical sciences deal with the 'laws of nature,' with the repetition of facts under given circumstances, not only in the past but also in the future; history deals with isolated facts of the past, facts which cannot be repeated and hence cannot be thoroughly verified. At first view it seems impossible to bridge that abyss. And yet the difference is perhaps quantitative rather than qualitative. For, on the one hand, historical facts are more or less repeated. When a tyrannical rule is introduced into a country, one or more of certain well known series of events are bound to happen in consequence of it. The repetition is not complete and detailed, as in the case of physical or chemical facts, yet there is a repetition of patterns which deserves to be taken into account. The trouble with the Carlyle-Poincaré example is that it is too particular; it would be too particular even for the physicist. John Lackland will never come again; but there may be others like him, and patterns of a definite kind will entail a succession of other definite patterns. On the other hand, on account of the infinite complexity of causes and of the dissipation of energy, physical events never repeat themselves exactly. The planets do not follow twice the same trajectories.

The old saying of Heraclitus is truer than ever: Πάντα ῥεῖ,

---

[1] *La Science et l'Hypothèse*, p. 168.

everything flows. The physical world is less regular and
the social world more regular than one generally admits,
and thus the two are not so widely apart as we imagine.

As opposed to the more exact mathematical sciences, the
historical 'sciences' seem to usurp their name, but it is not
fair to compare the extremes of a series. A comparison with
the natural sciences is more adequate. The historian of
science, to return to him, is a collector of scientific ideas in
the same way that the entomologist is a collector of insects,
the 'collection' in both cases being only the first step along
the road to knowledge. The point is that both will use similar methods to make sure that the items of their collections
are as unequivocally and completely determined as possible,
and when the facts are duly established they must needs use
similar methods to draw their conclusions and to build up
progressively a system of knowledge. The comparison of the
historian with the naturalist might be pursued retrospectively at different stages of their growth. There was a time
of innocence when their methods were equally immature
and inconclusive; both have learned gradually, very gradually, to make the most of the available evidence, the most
but not more, and even to measure to some extent their
approximation to the truth. Under the healthful influence
of geological and prehistoric research, some historians have
now become full brothers to naturalists.

The prehistorians and other archaeologists have built a
solid bridge between history and science, and we, historians
of science, are now proceeding to build another one, even
more substantial, and thus to help span the chasm which is
cutting our culture asunder and threatening to destroy it.
The scientific spirit is as much improved and purified by the
admixture of historical considerations as is humanism itself
by the introduction of scientific methods.

* * *

The main point to emphasize — and if this is properly
understood all the rest follows without difficulty — is that

accuracy is as fundamental in the historical field as in the scientific one, and that it has the same meaning in both fields. He may state that I should trouble to explain what to them is obvious, but it is necessary to do so in order to eradicate the prejudices of scientists against us, and enable them to come and meet the historians of science half way, instead of throwing spokes into our wheels.

Let us suppose that a physicist has to measure the length or distance *AB*. He may state that *AB* is 3 m. long, or 300 cm., or 3000 mm. These are three different statements, for they imply different degrees of accuracy: in the last case, for example, that the length is correct within a millimetre (2999 mm. $< AB <$ 3001 mm.). The degree of accuracy obtainable or desirable varies with the circumstances, but one must be accurate within the limits which are appropriate and which are suggested by the choice of units or the number of decimals.

The situation is exactly the same with regard to dates. If you state that a certain event happened on October 20, 1495 (Gregorian), you must be reasonably sure that it is the 20th, not the 19th or the 21st. A scientist, however meticulous he may be in his own field, will shrug his shoulders and grumble: "What do I care whether it is the 20th or the 25th. . . ." Very well. It may indeed be of no importance, but then why state the day? Why not say "October, 1495," or "1495," or "toward the end of the fifteenth century"? The last statement might be the best one. To say "Oct. 20, 1495," when you are not sure of the day, is nothing but a lie, just as if you said that *AB* was 3000 mm. long after a perfunctory measurement with a draper's yardstick. To affect a higher degree of precision than one can vouch for is just as reprehensible in the one case as in the other. Dates can be determined with reference to a definite calendar by means of authentic documents, or by means of coincidences with other events duly dated, or by a more complicated system of deductions. In every case they are determined within certain limits, and we are bound to state them as correctly as is possible within these limits, the limits themselves being indicated by the choice of units or more explicitly.

I have selected these two examples, lengths and dates, because they are exceedingly simple and yet fundamental. Physical measurements are generally reduced to measurements of length (linear or angular; on the object itself or on our instruments); as to the dates, they are to the historian what spherical coördinates are to the geographer or the astronomer. Nothing in either case could be more fundamental. More technical examples could not provide better illustrations of the argument, for these hit the root of the matter: precision has the same meaning in history as in science, and entails the same obligations.

It is true the errors of historians may remain unnoticed; they cannot be found out as easily as the scientific ones (some of the latter would be almost automatically detected sooner or later); but this does not decrease the historian's responsibility; it increases it.

In physical measurements, the readings of our instruments need correction. If we measure the length of a bar of metal, we must take the temperature into account, and reduce our sundry readings to the same temperature. If we measure the coördinates of stars, we must take into account the aberration of light, the nutation of the earth's axis, the atmospheric refraction, the systematic errors of our instruments, our personal equation. Similar corrections may have to be made with regard to dates; these cannot be compared without having been properly reduced and inserted in the same chronological series. Moreover the date which we read in a book or document may not be correct; it may be vitiated by accidental or systematic errors.

To illustrate. One of the earliest printed editions of Ptolemy's *Geography* bears on its colophon the date 1462 (see Fig. 1). It has been proved that that date is certainly wrong; the real date is probably 1477.[1] With the clumsy Roman numerals such errors were easy enough. If the printed date were true, that edition would be the *princeps*, which it is not. The first dated edition was printed at Vicenza in 1475, without maps; the first edition with maps

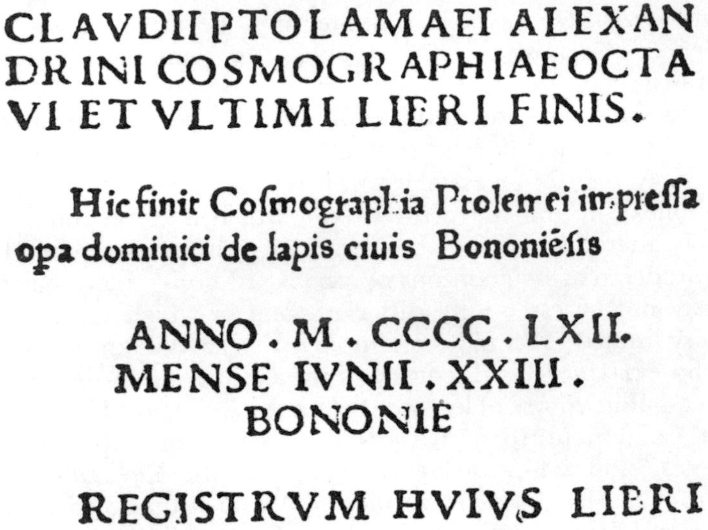

CLAVDII PTOLAMAEI ALEXAN DRINI COSMOGRAPHIAE OCTA VI ET VLTIMI LIERI FINIS.

Hic finit Cofmographia Ptolemei impreffa opa dominici de lapis ciuis Bononiéfis

ANNO . M . CCCC . LXII. MENSE IVNII . XXIII. BONONIE

REGISTRVM HVIVS LIERI

FIG. 1. — Colophon of an early edition of Ptolemy's *Geography*, printed in Bologna probably in 1477. The date of the colophon, 1462, is certainly wrong. (Courtesy of the John Carter Brown Library in Providence, R. I., and of Prof. R. C. Archibald).

is the Roman of 1478. In such cases as this, the historian must disbelieve what he sees, and discover more or less painfully the real truth behind the apparent one. He must do with other methods what the physicist is often doing in his own province.

For the period posterior to the invention of printing, the

[1] Sarton, *Introduction*, vol. 1, p. 275, giving 1482 as the date. For the more probable date 1477 see Lino Sighinolfi, "I mappamondi di Taddeo Crivelli e la stampa bolognese della Cosmografia di Tolomeo," in *La bibliofilía*, anno x, pp. 241–269 (1908).

date of the first printed publication of a discovery is generally assumed to be the date of that discovery. However, there are snares for the unwary, and the rule needs many qualifications. For instance, the cautious historian is aware that the dates printed on the covers of periodicals are not always truthful, and when delicate questions of priority are involved these printed dates cannot be accepted as evidence; one must take the trouble of determining the dates of issue.[1]

In some cases the publication of a discovery has occurred *viva voce* in a public lecture or at the meeting of an academy. It may then be necessary to distinguish between that oral publication and the printed one, which may be considerably altered and delayed. These two publications should be considered as two editions of a book, editions which may or may not be essentially different, and of which the first is very limited. A famous example is that of William Harvey, who explained his discovery of the circulation of the blood in a public course of lectures before the College of Physicians in London in 1616, witness his own manuscript lecture notes,[2] and again twelve years later in the *Exercitatio Anatomica de Motu Cordis et Sanguinis*. We must thus distinguish two publications: the first, oral, in 1616 to a limited circle of London practitioners; the second, through a book printed in Frankfort in 1628, to the whole republic of letters. There

---

[1] Sometimes the date of issue is stated on the cover, but that is not conclusive. The issue may be postponed at the eleventh hour for the sake of an important correction or addition, and the date left as it was. In many great libraries, the dates of reception of individual numbers are often marked by means of a rubber stamp: the date of issue may then be deduced from such dates of reception.

The Société Asiatique of Paris is a great offender in this respect. For instance, the two numbers constituting vol. 235 of the *Journal asiatique* and bearing the dates "juillet–septembre 1934" and "octobre–décembre 1934" were actually received by me in Cambridge, Massachusetts, in March and June, 1935. Scholars might eventually claim on the basis of such arbitrary and misleading dating a priority which they would not deserve.

[2] Charles Singer, *The Discovery of the Circulation of the Blood* (London, 1922; cf. *Isis*, vol. 5, pp. 194–196). See also Sir William Maddock Bayliss, *Principles of General Physiology*, 4th ed. (London, 1924), pp. 666–669.

is no evidence that the first ephemeral publication had any influence; the second being permanent could wait; its influence was felt very slowly and gradually, but irresistibly.

For another illustration of the constant need of vigilance, let us turn to tombstones. We are all cautious enough with regard to the moral judgments included in epitaphs. We know that the 'devoted husband' may have been a libertine, and the 'beloved and respected father' a selfish tyrant, but we are singularly prone to accept the dates carved on stones as correct. Even so great a scholar as the late Percy Stafford Allen, the editor of Erasmus's letters, made the following imprudent remarks apropos of the tomb of Alonso de Fonseca, archbishop of Seville (died 1473), which he visited in the castle of Coca. "Here on his tomb was an authority beyond which we need not seek, the date of his death graven securely on stone." [1] If the tomb was built within the year of death, we may perhaps assume that the date is correctly graven, though the stone cutter might forget one of the many items of a Roman date as easily as the printer; if the tomb was built some time later, as often happened, the causes of error increase. I have already quoted the case of that heroic Transylvanian scholar, Körösi Csoma Sándor.[2] A monument to his memory in Darjeeling, Sikkim, proclaims the following, "On his road to H'Lassa to resume his labours he died at this place on the 11th April 1842, aged 44 years" (see Fig. 2, borrowed from Theodore Duka's biography, 1885, p. 154). Now we know that Csoma was born in 1784; he was then 58 years old at the time of his death, not 44.

The moral of this is that the historian, like his brother scientist, must accept nothing without investigation and verification; he must be forever on the alert, and nurse skepticism in his mind until every suspicion has been dis-

[1] P. S. Allen, *Erasmus, Lectures and Wayfaring Sketches* (Oxford, 1934), p. 188.
[2] Sarton, "Preface to Volume Twelve," in *Isis*, vol. 12, pp. 5–9 (1929). See also *Isis*, vol. 16, p. 180.

pelled. In practice it is obviously impossible to verify every-thing, but the experienced and wise historian knows when to relax his vigilance and when to intensify it. The differ-ence between careless and careful work is of exactly the same order in the field of history as in that of science. Care-

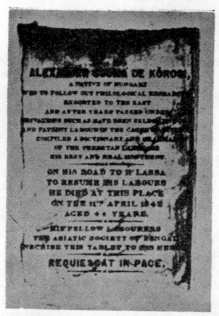

FIG. 2. — Epitaph on the monument to Alexander Csoma in Darjeeling. The implied date of birth is wrong.

less work is easy enough, while every additional precaution increases the difficulty, the slowness, and the tediousness of the endeavor. Even as the good scientist must be prepared to take infinite pains and work over endless trivialities in order to be sure of the accuracy of his experiments, even so the historian must be ready to check and recheck, in as many ways as are available, countless details, each of which may seem unimportant. Unfortunately the law of diminishing return applies to historical research as well as to scientific research. Beyond a certain point additional refinement becomes increasingly more expensive, and after a while the expense becomes prohibitive. Long before reaching that limit, the work may become so hard and boresome that its value may be questioned. "Is all that travail worth while?" sighs the fagged scholar in a moment of despair. It *is* worth while, for, in history as in science, inaccurate data are of no value. However cheaply the latter may be bought, their price is too high, while truth, or even the nearest approach to it that can be won, is never too dear, for it is beyond price.

One should, indeed, avoid needless precision, but historians, like scientists, hesitate to draw the line, and for the same reasons. We may not need a high degree of precision for our own investigations, but no one can foretell the degree of precision which may be needed later on for other investigations. Moreover, it is always possible to deduce less precise data from more precise ones, while the contrary is impossible. If we have found the length of a wire to be 1998 mm., we can say later that it was two metres long; but if we put on record a length of two metres and lose the wire, it will remain forever impossible to indicate its length in millimetres. If we know that Copernicus died on May 24, 1543,[1] we can always simplify that statement, and say that he died in May, 1543, or in 1543, or toward the middle of the sixteenth century, which would suffice in many cases, but we could not reverse the procedure. Accordingly it is generally advisable to adapt our precision not so much to our immediate need as to our power of attainment.

The average degree of precision in historical investigations is unfortunately much smaller than that within the reach of the physicist, the chemist, or even the physiologist. The story has often been told of how Sir Walter Ralegh, on receiving I forget how many different accounts of an inci-

---

[1] For a discussion of this date see Leopold Prowe, *Nicolaus Coppernicus* (Berlin, 1883), vol. 1, part 2, pp. 554–556.

dent which he had witnessed from his own window at the Tower, laughed at the idea of his writing a history of the world. And yet he did write it! No scientist worth his salt has ever abandoned an investigation simply because the attainable precision was too low. Our duty is to be as accurate as we can; it is independent of the absolute degree of accuracy. Our merit is in every case proportional to the ratio of the amount of truth which we discover to the amount discoverable.

In the search after truth, one can never be too cautious or too humble. The good scientist understands that very well in his own domain, but he is likely to throw humility and prudence to the winds when he deals with historical subjects. Now this is intolerable and indefensible. He is not obliged to do historical work; but if he does, he should remain faithful to his own standards of accuracy and honesty, or else be freely castigated and discredited. Careless historical work is as contemptible as careless experimental work, and errors due to the neglect of well known historical methods are as disgraceful as errors due to the neglect of well known experimental methods.

When the scientist realizes all this, and becomes aware of the existence of historical pitfalls similar to the ones wherewith he is familiar in his own laboratory, he is on the road to wisdom, and when he develops a historical conscience as well as a scientific one, his new education may be said to be well begun and his initiation into humanistic studies prepared in the best manner.

It is obviously out of the question in these few introductory pages to describe our field of study even in outline, but I shall try to give an idea of the immensity of our field and of the complexity and variety of our interests. The historian of science must consider the development of science and technique from the earliest beginnings down to our own days, in all countries, and by people of all races and all faiths; he must consider the development of science at every time and in every place. He must be prepared to extend his investigations as deeply into the past as the emergence of human documents allows, and yet keep his scientific knowledge as up-to-date as possible. To be sure, nobody is supposed to know equally well the development of every science at every time, but the professional historian of science should have some knowledge of the whole field, even as the astronomer, no matter how narrow his special interest may be, is expected to have a general knowledge of astronomy.

The most severe of these requirements is perhaps the one concerning the living and ever expanding science of our time. It is hard enough for the specialist to keep abreast of the steady progress of his own field of study, and yet he is only expected to survey a relatively small sector of the whole horizon. The historian of science should have some acquaintance with the whole field of advancing knowledge, with all the frontiers of science, though he can hardly be expected to enter into technicalities. This obligation rests upon his shoulders because the more he knows of the science of to-day, the better will he be able to appreciate that of the past; early science was once alive, even as our own will soon be dead, and to understand the life of science we must observe it as it grows around us. Could the palaeobotanist understand fossil plants if he were not familiar with living ones? This requirement is difficult enough for the historian of science who has laid a serious scientific foundation to his studies; it is hopelessly beyond the reach of the one who lacks such foundation. Without a sufficient knowledge of modern science, he is unable to understand earlier stages of knowledge, or what is worse, when he believes that he understands, he is almost bound to misunderstand. One of the most pernicious types of error to which a false or shaky knowledge of living science frequently leads is the reading of modern conceptions, such as atomic ideas, energy, evolution, into ancient texts. Nationalist or religious prejudices have often exposed Hindus or Muslims to errors of that very kind, and some western scholars have been caught in the same trap because of their irrational love for the Middle Ages.

* * *

We shall realize in another way the immensity of our task when we try to divide it, as we must, either for study or teaching. Moot points arise at once. How shall we divide the past? How shall we define intervals of equal importance? One might be tempted as a first approximation to give equal importance to periods of equal length, but the result of this would be to give to ancient times an exaggerated importance, and to eclipse the astounding achievements of our own days. Many scientists and philosophers seem to believe that 'real' science dates only from the seventeenth or sixteenth century. Even a superficial knowledge of ancient history is sufficient to prove the falseness and the absurdity of that belief, but it is a demonstrable fact that the progress of science is constantly accelerated,[1] and hence that more and more is accomplished in shorter and shorter periods.

To show how much our perspective of the past would be distorted by an assumption of its homogeneity, let us assume that the total past to be taken into account measures 5400 years — fifty-four centuries, hardly more than two hundred generations, if as many — that is, let us begin our history c. 3415 B.C. Then, on a full circumference, each year would be represented by four minutes, each century by 6° 40'. Our three golden centuries, the seventeenth to the nineteenth, would occupy a sector of only 20°! (Fig. 3). And that assumption, it should be noted, would be very far from

---

[1] The acceleration *seems* to have diminished about 1882 (see below), but that is another story.

satisfying to our prehistorians. They would say, "3415 B.C.! That is hardly more than yesterday in the story of human evolution! By that time *the main work was already done*, and had been done for ages, for it is the first steps which are the most difficult as well as the most de-

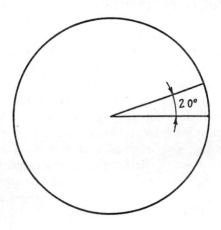

Fig. 3

Sector of 20°, representing three centuries if 360° = 5400 years.

cisive." The history of science must be made to begin with the fundamental inventions: language, drawing, writing, artificial fire, elementary tools, etc. The unknown fire-makers and the inventors of the wheel were the true ancestors of our Edisons and Marconis, and not a bit inferior to them. It required, probably, more genius to invent the first wheel than the latest dynamo. We should begin our survey at least half a million years ago. If we assumed a length of about 648,000 years for the whole record down to now, then on a full circumference each year would be represented by two seconds, and our glorious twentieth century, so full in spite of its youth of tremendous discoveries, by hardly more than a minute, so that it would not appear at all even on a large sized figure.[1]

* * *

I have insisted upon this simply to help in correcting the opposite error of perspective usually made by scientists. Their tendency is to divide the past, not into periods of equal length, but into periods of equal productivity. On that basis the ancient times and the Middle Ages are entirely sacrificed to our more immediate past, when the slow gestation of centuries and millenaries was suddenly followed by an amazing outburst of discoveries.

Let us see how their conception works. A convenient measure is provided by Ludwig Darmstaedter's *Handbuch zur Geschichte der Naturwissenschaften und der Technik* (2d ed., Berlin, 1908), a list of discoveries enumerated year by year from c. 3500 B.C. to 1908 A.D., a total of 5407 years or 54 centuries. I give below the number of pages and the percentage devoted to successive periods:

TABLE I

35 centuries B.C.	28 pages	3%
Cents. I to XV................	43	4
XVI	33	3
XVII	55	5
XVIII	117	11
XIX	717	67
Years 1901–08	77	7
	1070 pages	100 %

[1] Here is another illustration of the same idea given by J. H. Robinson. "Let us imagine . . . that 500,000 years of developing culture were compressed into 50 years. On this scale mankind would have required 49 years to learn enough to desert here and there his inveterate hunting habits and settle down in villages. Half through the fiftieth year writing was discovered and practised within a very limited area, thus supplying one of the chief means for perpetuating and spreading culture. The achievements of the Greeks would be but three months back, the prevailing of Christianity, two; the printing press would be a fortnight old and man would have been using steam for hardly a week. The peculiar conditions under which we live did not come about until Dec. 31 of the fiftieth year." "Civilization," in *Encyclopaedia Britannica*, 14th ed. (London, 1929), vol. 5, p. 738.

That is, the earliest fifty centuries out of fifty-four (93%) are disposed of in less than 7% of the total space, while the nineteenth century alone (less than 2%) covers 67% of it!

Or, to put it in another way, let us divide the *Handbuch* into sections of a hundred pages each, and see to how many years each of these sections corresponds, in absolute numbers and percentages.

TABLE II

Pp. 1–100, c. 3500 B.C. to 1591 A.D., 5090 years		94.14%
Pp. 101–200, to 1756 165		3.05
Pp. 201–300, to 1809 53		.96
Pp. 301–400, to 1832 23		.44
Pp. 401–500, to 1847 15		.28
Pp. 501–600, to 1860 13		.24
Pp. 601–700, to 1872 12		.22
Pp. 701–800, to 1882 10		.18
Pp. 801–900, to 1891 9		.17
Pp. 901–1000, to 1901 10		.18
Pp. 1001–1070, to 1908 .... (7) [1]		.14
	5407 years	100.00 %

[1] The annual rate for this period is about the same as for the thirty years previous.

That is, the first hundred pages deal with 94% of the total time, the first three hundred pages (28% of the book) with 98% of the total time, while the rest of the book (72%) deals only with the last 2% of the fifty-four centuries.

Table II is very interesting, because, if the data upon which it is based are correct, — and they may be considered so at least for a first approximation, — the acceleration in the progress of science did *not* continue to increase after, say, c. 1882. It should be noted in passing that the amazing acceleration in the rate of discoveries and inventions in the nineteenth century was partly mechanical: it was due to the increase in the number of universities, laboratories, and investigators. It is clear that to determine the natural acceleration it would be necessary to make allowance for the artificial acceleration due to the multiplication of centres of research and of experts. However, if the purpose is to measure the acceleration of scientific progress by whatever means, then the figures of Table II do not need such correction.

* * *

It is clear enough that this last picture, which we may call, for short, the scientist's picture, is just as distorted as the former, which we may call the prehistorian's picture. The

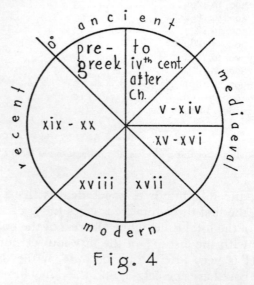

Fig. 4

true picture must be somewhere in between, though a precise determination of it is obviously out of the question. Indeed, there are no accurate means of measuring the value of past achievements. Bearing always in mind that initial efforts are by far the most difficult, and, in general, that equal efforts made at different times should be given very different weights, and that equal efforts made in different countries, or under different circumstances, have also very different weights, our division of the past must be necessarily rough and tentative.

A scholar's intuition may well provide the best answer, the value of his answer being a function of his experience and wisdom. My experience extends over twenty-five years, during which I have been obliged not only to lecture

Fig. 5

on a great many subjects, covering among them almost the whole field, but also to examine a very large proportion of the writings devoted to our studies by scholars of almost every civilized country. My own solution may thus deserve to be considered. I have really two solutions between which I often hesitate and which are best represented by the two diagrams above (Figs. 4 and 5). The main difference between these two diagrams lies in the last quadrant, which in Fig. 4 is devoted to recent times only, the last 135 years, while in Fig. 5 it includes the eighteenth century as well. It any case these diagrams should not be taken too literally; they are nothing more than suggestions of how to balance the past against the present.

Many scholars, I am sure, would wish to increase the share allotted to Greek science (only half a quadrant) at the expense of the Middle Ages. They would have good reasons for doing so, for the scientific achievements of the Greeks and of the Hellenistic age were incomparably greater than those of all the centuries following until the seventeenth. It should not be forgotten, however, that in any full account of mediaeval science much space is necessarily devoted to the transmission of ancient science and its discussion. Even as Greek science was preceded by an enormously long period of preparation, which deserves careful study (we give half a quadrant to it in both schemas), even so the Middle Ages was the time of gestation of modern science. It was a new incubation of all ideas inherited from the near and distant past and of newer ideas gradually added to the mixture. The study of mediaeval tradition and invention is not so thrilling as the Greek miracle, but it is very important in another way and very interesting. A relatively large amount of time is needed to explain it, because the story cannot be tolerably complete without a full account of Oriental (chiefly Arabic) science, and the disentanglement of every skein of tradition is very complicated.

The question which we have just discussed, the proper division of the past, is not only of theoretical but also of practical interest, for every professor of the history of science, and every author of a textbook which is supposed to cover the whole field or a large part of it, must decide how he will divide his time or his text. Whenever I have to review a book dealing with the history of science in general, my first test of it is almost always to find out how the author solved this fundamental problem; his solution gives me valuable information with regard to his tendencies, experience, and wisdom.

* * *

Though a teacher of the subject may have to cover the whole field, he cannot be expected to have a first-hand and deep knowledge of every part of it, any more than the professor of general chemistry, let us say, can be expected to have a first-hand knowledge of the whole of chemistry. However, in this case as in others, first-hand and experimental knowledge of one part of the field enables one to appreciate more critically other parts of it, though one's familiarity with them must necessarily remain very imperfect.

One of the best means of obtaining a relative mastery of the whole field is to make judicious cross-sections of it, and every scholar engaged in these studies should try to carry out as far as possible three different types of cross-sections and to remain sufficiently familiar with them throughout life. He should make a special study of:

(1) The development of one branch of science, say, astronomy, or of a smaller field, say, geodesy.

(2) The development of science and learning during a special period, say, the fourteenth century.

(3) The development of science and learning within a certain country, or by the people of a special race or faith, or by the people using a special language. E. g., Italian science, Arabic or Islamic science, the scientific content of post-classical Latin literature.

The well tempered historian of science who has become sufficiently familiar with three such sections might be said to be adequately prepared, though his actual mastery of the subject would naturally depend upon his experience, diligence, and wisdom.

It should be noted that the three perpendicular sections are not artificial. On the contrary, almost every scholar exploring the field with some method would be irresistibly led to the employment of the three kinds. To begin with, his own scientific preparation would introduce the first cross-section. If he had obtained his main scientific experience in mathematics, he would naturally be more interested in the history of mathematics than of other sciences and better equipped to study it. His own nationality or race would determine the second cross-section. If he were an Italian, he would be more interested in Italian science and more competent to deal with it. The reading of old MSS. is always a good deal easier for one who has a native knowledge of the language than for any other scholar, however well the latter may fancy he knows it. The use of libraries, archives, and collections, and the tracking down of documents is also much easier and more fruitful for a native or citizen of the country involved than for a foreigner. The choice of the horizontal cross-section is perhaps a little more arbitrary, though it would be partly determined by the two other sections. A student of the history of mathematics would be easily fascinated by the golden age of Greek mathematics, or by the seventeenth century, and would desire to know other aspects of those privileged periods than the purely mathematical; or if he were a Muslim, an Arab, or an Arabist he would wish to explore more completely the age when Arabic culture was supreme. These three cross-sections, it should be noted, are never independent; each includes projections of the two others and completes them (Fig. 6).

* * *

What I have said thus far illustrates not merely the immensity of our field, but also its endless and bewildering variety. Such subjects as, let us say, Greek geometry, Chinese alchemy, Hindu astronomy, seismology, and internal secretions are as different as can be; they imply not only different equipments but different attitudes of mind.

So large and complex is the field, that though I have explored it during a quarter of a century in almost every conceivable direction, I would not dare say that I know it. The difficulties are caused partly by its complexity and infinite

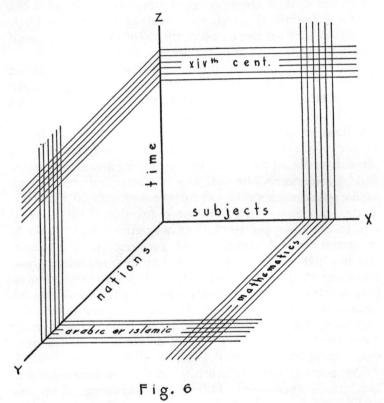

Fig. 6

variety, partly by the lack of tools, due to the very youthfulness of our discipline.

It is worth while to stop here for a moment and consider our lack of tools. Though the great men of science are in their own unobtrusive way the leaders of mankind, and must be counted among its foremost benefactors, there are relatively few full-sized biographies devoted to them, and in many cases we even lack short ones that are, at the same time, accurate. There are many collections of such biographies, but the bulk of them are meretricious little books, which may satisfy the average reader, but are of no value for the historian. Even at their best, as in Cuvier's *Éloges historiques*, they do not measure up to the standards of good biography obtaining in other fields.

Take another type of monograph, the study of separate questions, as, e. g., the discovery of specific and latent heats.[1] To be sure, most of these studies are contributions to the history of particular branches of science, but the main questions of each science concern the whole of science. Problems of specific and latent heat are not the affair of physicists only, but also of chemists, geologists, astronomers, and physiologists. The best way to realize our lack of such fundamental monographs is to take any general textbook. The experienced reader will soon notice that there is hardly a page or paragraph which does not require, for the sake of completeness and accuracy, the preparation of a monograph which does not yet exist. Strictly speaking, those textbooks should not be written until the necessary monographs were ready as a foundation; strictly speaking, the elementary books should be the last to be composed; but their premature publication cannot be helped, for we need them right away; at every level of our growth we need syntheses to guide our new analytic efforts.

The point to keep in mind is that the work remaining to be done is enormous. This is not surprising when one realizes, on the one hand, the immensity of the task, and on the other the fewness of the workers, as compared with the legions of other historians engaged in the study of political or economic history, the history of religions, of art, of lan-

---

[1] This particular topic comes to my mind because it has recently been treated with great care by Douglas McKie and Niels H. de V. Heathcote (London, 1935; cf. *Isis*, vol. 25, p. 227).

guages and literatures, of arts and crafts, in short, of everything except of that which is the backbone of culture: science.

As one question after another is investigated down to bed rock, as better textbooks and treatises are gradually produced, and syntheses of larger and larger fields made at higher and higher levels, it will become easier to know the whole subject. The total knowledge will be very much larger and more precise, but it will be so clarified and so well ordered that its comprehension will be simpler.

* * *

We shall understand this better if we make a distinction between what I should call real knowledge and potential knowledge. For example, if I owned a book containing a list of all countries and cities of the world with their positions, areas, and populations, all according to the latest and most authoritative sources, if there were such a gazetteer at my elbow, I could say that I had a potential knowledge of its contents, for pertinent information of the best kind could be extracted from it immediately, as one would extract it from one's memory. In fact, such a book might be considered an extension of one's memory, though far more reliable than the best memory could ever be. This is an extreme case; passing to the other extreme, it is equally true that the possession of the best textbook on the theory of functions would not give me *ipso facto* any potential knowledge of the subject. If I had made years ago a thorough study of it, and since then forgotten most of it, my real knowledge would be dwindling to zero, but the textbook might replace it by a potential knowledge. In this case, however, the potential knowledge would not have been obtained gratis, as in the first one, but only at the price of long antecedent efforts.

The branches of science and learning might all be ar-

ranged in a single row according to the degree of availability of potential knowledge, the ones where that degree is
lowest, the mathematical branches, being placed at the
extreme left, the ones where that degree is highest at the
extreme right. Happily for us, the historical sciences would
find their proper place toward the right end. In other
words, a fair amount of historical knowledge is immediately
available to any intelligent man owning the proper tools.
The special tools of the historian of science are not yet
ready — or, at least, very few of them —, but they can be
made, and will probably be available to the next, or next
but one, generation of scholars. When his own good tools
are finally ready for him, and he has been trained in their
use, a large amount of potential knowledge will be open to
him. To be sure, a treatise on the history of mathematics
will not be immediately helpful to the non-mathematician,
but it will extend with little effort the potential knowledge
of the historically-minded mathematician.

* * *

To return to our subject. However difficult the determination of scientific facts of the past may be, e. g., the definition of a discovery and its correct placing and dating,
their interpretation and final appreciation are exceedingly
more difficult, and especially so because in this case historical rules and methods are of little avail; what is needed
is the total scientific and historical experience of the judge,
the wisdom and subtlety of his mind, the charity of his heart.
Here is a fact. On March 13, 1781, William Herschel discovered a "curious either nebulous star or perhaps a
comet" which turned out to be a new planet, Uranus.
What does that mean? In order to appreciate it, one must
bear in mind the history of astronomy down to that time
and realize that this was the first planet to be discovered
within the memory of mankind! One must bear in mind

the circumstances of Herschel's life and activity. How did he discover Uranus, and why did nobody else discover it before him? What were the implications, for him and others, for us, of that discovery? The statement of the discovery is almost meaningless, unless all these explanations are implicitly available to the reader, or explicitly stated to him. A bare fact is nothing, though its potentialities may be endless; meaningless to one person, it opens up to another a new chapter of science or life, and provides the kernel of a tragedy. The historico-scientific facts are the stones of the building which the historian of science is building; if accurate, they are invaluable — history without them is nothing but a vision, a dream, a bubble, a shadow, and even less, the shadow of a shadow; yet they are worthless unless placed in their proper sequence and position, each one being explained and justified by all the others.

* * *

The search for new historical materials is itself a task of great complexity, to the extent that only a part of it, and that not the most important, can be taught. However, the teachable part should be learned; the delicate methods involved are explained in historical seminars or in special textbooks. We cannot insist upon that. When the historian of science has finally succeeded in tracking down some new document, by the use of such methods or his own shrewdness, or both, his next task is to criticize it, externally and internally, and to make the best use of it. If he be dealing with an early text, which may be represented by more than one MS., he must first 'establish' it, that is, he must determine the most probable text. Of course, the establishment of a scientific text, its external and internal criticisms, are not different from those relative to any other texts. The methods are exactly the same, but the internal criticism, i. e., the interpretation of the contents, will neces-

sarily require an adequate knowledge of the scientific ideas
involved and of their implications. To appreciate a scientific text fairly, it does not suffice to know how much of it is
true from our more advanced point of view, we must find
out how much of it was considered true at the time of its
composition, how much was true or plausible within the
framework of contemporary science, how much was new.
What were its sources? What was its influence? Two questions which seem very simple, yet either of which may involve endless investigation. We must reconstruct link by
link the sequences of ideas leading to that text, and the new
sequences leading from it. We must place that text as
exactly as possible within the complicated network of our
traditions.

This is, again, a set of problems with which historians are
familiar enough, and scientists unfamiliar. Modern scientists hardly think of tradition, because it is now insured by
various competitive agencies. The average scientist need
not worry about it; as far as he is concerned, the tradition is
almost automatic. It might be interrupted here or there by
some physical or social disaster; it could hardly be stopped
everywhere and forever. A geologist who takes the trouble
of examining a few geological journals of various countries
knows almost everything that is being done within his field
and is worth knowing. Should an exceptional discovery or
a startling theory be published — say, the Wegener hypothesis — he would hear of it not only once, but a hundred
times; his own newspaper would speak of it; indeed, he
would have to stop his ears not to hear of it.

Conditions were very different before the existence of
scientific journals; they were worse still before the invention
of printing. The tradition of knowledge in ancient times
and even in the Middle Ages was exceedingly casual and
problematic; it might be jeopardized at any time by a social
catastrophe if not by a trivial accident; at best it was very
slow and irregular. Indeed, when one thinks of all the

vicissitudes of ancient history it seems almost miraculous that so many early texts — say, abstruse mathematical treatises which could not interest many people and were never represented by many MSS. — have come down to us. And those that have survived have reached us with almost unbelievable indirectness. For example, the treatises of Hippocrates, Aristotle, Galen, originally written in Greek, were translated into Syriac, then into Arabic (or directly into Arabic), then into Hebrew and into Latin (or into both), then into our own vernaculars. Each of these stages entailed errors of omission or commission, each translation was somewhat of a gamble, each edition was represented by divergent manuscripts, and so forth.

When one visualizes all these hazards and perils, is it not astounding that we are able to read and enjoy to-day a treatise which Archimedes wrote twenty-two centuries ago?

It is true that the ideas which the ancient treatises contained may have trickled down to us in countless other ways. The historian's task is then not simply to determine the contents of Ptolemy's knowledge, but to trace the tangled channels through which that knowledge has reached modern astronomers such as Copernicus, and how its mixture with other intellectual streams of equally complicated ancestry has helped to constitute, very gradually, our own conceptions. Ptolemy's works are one thing, their tradition quite another, both indispensable. When we are told that our energy is derived from the sun, we are not satisfied until we are shown how that energy is communicated. It is a very complicated story; the history of the Ptolemaic tradition is equally complicated and fascinating.

* * *

As the historian is expected to determine not only the relative truth of scientific ideas at different chronological stages, but also their relative novelty, he is irresistibly led to the fixation of *first* events. "So-and-so was the first to do this-or-that." "This was the first treatise dealing with . . ." This never fails to involve him in new difficulties, because creations absolutely *de novo* are very rare, if they occur at all; most novelties are only novel combinations of old elements, and the degree of novelty is thus a matter of interpretation, which may vary considerably according to the historian's experience, standpoint, or prejudices. At any rate the determination of an event as the 'first' is not a special affirmation relative to that event, but a general negative proposition relative to an undetermined number of unknown events. It is always risky, yet when every reasonable precaution has been taken one must be willing to run the risk and make the challenge, for this is the only means of being corrected, if correction be needed.

We remarked a moment ago that scientific tradition has now become almost automatic; we may be sure that scientific novelties will almost inevitably be known within a short interval of time to the scientists working along the same lines. However, the problem of tradition reappears in another form, which may leave the pure scientist curiously indifferent, but touches the humanist on the raw. How is scientific knowledge transmitted, not to the specialists (that is easy enough), but to other scientists, and, most difficult of all, to non-scientists? How is scientific knowledge to be taught to children, how is it to be diffused to the educated world? And, most pregnant question of all, how can scientific methods and points of view be inculcated in people's minds?

Most educators, not to speak of non-educators, have false notions on the diffusion of scientific knowledge. It is very important that every man should be made to realize the immensity of the universe, and the inverse immensity of atoms, but does it really matter how many know the latest size of the universe, or are able to describe accurately the latest atomic models? Most of the newest knowledge, the kind that is featured in newspapers, is of little concern to all but specialists. On the other hand, it is of fundamental importance that every educated man and woman should be made to understand the methods of scientific research, and be trained to love truth irrespective of his interests and prejudices. There is nothing impossible in that; that is, it should not be more difficult to teach people not to lie, than not to steal. The principles and methods of science could be taught any sound-minded person with only a fraction of the effort that is now misused to teach him the newest particularities which he does not really need. The teaching should be concentrated on the facts and theories which have survived the controversial stage and have (or should have) become part and parcel of the common knowledge of educated men all over the world. The experimental proof and the explanation of those facts and theories (either in the historical order or otherwise) would serve to illustrate the methods and spirit of science. The republic requires relatively few scientists, but it will not be healthy until a majority, or at least a large minority, of its citizens have been trained to consider every-day problems, and to judge political and social controversies, with a certain degree of objectivity and disinterestedness.

* * *

The mention of scientific methods suggests another aspect of our investigations: the study of the development of science from the logical point of view. The fact that the logic of science is largely casual and retrospective does not matter. It remains of great interest to discover inductively the logical sequences or the logical solutions of continuity in the arguments and activities which have led mankind from one discovery into another, and from each scientific level up to a higher one indefinitely. We can thus reconstruct, or help to reconstruct, as it were, the development of the human genius; that is, not the intelligence of any single man or group of men, but that of mankind as a whole. It is clear that this field of inquiries provides a necessary complement to purely historical investigations, and that it is in itself so large that a scholar's life would be too short to explore it completely.

However averse the historian may be to philosophical and logical discussions, he cannot eschew them altogether, because he cannot properly appreciate the value of discoveries without them. To illustrate this let us consider for a moment the idea of *experimentum crucis*. One calls a crucial experiment one which enables him to choose between hypotheses which are mutually exclusive by proving that one of them is right and that the other must be wrong. The classical example is that concerning the wave theory of light and the emission theory. There was much discussion in the first half of the nineteenth century as to which of those theories was right to the exclusion of the other. The latter had been favored by Newton and was generally accepted by the triumphant Newtonians; the first had been brilliantly but incompletely explained by Huygens, and after a century of neglect it had been revived by Young and almost completely vindicated by Fresnel. A few years after the latter's death, Sir William Rowan Hamilton in the course of his analytical development of the wave theory was able to predict the existence of a very rare kind of refraction, the conical refraction, which had never been observed. Hamilton's mathematical prediction of 1832 was verified experimentally by Humphrey Lloyd in the following year.[1] The wave theory seemed to be established on an inexpugnable basis, and yet some of the defenders of the emission theory refused

---

[1] For more details see G. Sarton, "Discovery of Conical Refraction" (*Isis*, vol. 17, pp. 154–170, 1932), including a facsimile of Lloyd's paper.

to capitulate. It was then that Arago invented an ingenious *experimentum crucis*. If the emission theory is correct, the speed of light must increase with the density of the medium; if the wave theory is correct, the speed must decrease with the density. Hence if we could measure the speed of light in air and water, the comparison of the results would tell us which theory was true. The extremely delicate experiments which he suggested were not realized until fifteen years later by Foucault, who proved that the speed of light is smaller in water than in air, and thus "that the emission theory is incompatible with the reality of the facts" (these are his own words).[1] This seemed to be decisive and final. There is no doubt that the emission theory was incompatible with the facts which he dealt with, but it did not follow that the wave theory was compatible with every other fact. To make a long story short, the study of black-body radiation revealed facts which were incompatible with the wave theory, and led to the formulation of the quantum theory by Max Planck in 1900.[2] Arago's *experimentum crucis* had simply proved that the wave theory was more complete than the emission theory, but it had not proved and could not prove that it was absolutely true.

It is clear that no experiment can be really 'crucial' until

[1] It is well to recall the three steps leading to that conclusion.

Charles Wheatstone, "An Account of some Experiments to Measure the Velocity of Electricity and the Duration of Electric Light" (*Philosophical Transactions*, 1834, pp. 583–591, 2 pl.). Explaining the method of rotating mirrors.

Arago, "Système d'expériences à l'aide duquel la théorie de l'émission et celle des ondes seront soumises à des épreuves décisives (*Annales de chimie et de physique*, vol. 71, pp. 49–65, 1839). Communicated in 1838. Arago explained the principle of the experiments and suggested their realization by means of Wheatstone's method.

Léon Foucault, "Sur les vitesses relatives de la lumière dans l'air et dans l'eau" (*Annales de chimie et de physique*, vol. 41, pp. 129–164, 1854). Realizing Arago's idea.

[2] For a good summary of this question, see F. K. Richtmyer, *Introduction to Modern Physics*, 2d ed. (New York, 1934), chapter 7 (*Isis*, vol. 24, pp. 172–174).

we are sure that our analysis of the possibilities is exhaustive, and this implies an omniscience which is hardly within our reach. Does this mean that the so-called crucial experiments are futile? Far from it: they help us to clear the ground; they enable us to continue further (if not to complete) the logical analysis of a set of problems, and incidentally to study the development of competitive theories and the reactions to them of different minds. The story of the Arago-Foucault experiments will always be one of the most beautiful in the history of mankind.

* * *

Another important concern of the logically-minded historian is the study of the interrelations between the different branches of science and of the gradual creation of new links between them. How did the progress of one science affect the progress of others? The methods which had been developed in a particular field, how were they applied, *mutatis mutandis*, to another, how could they conceivably be applied to others still? I am not prone to exaggerate, as Ostwald did,[1] the heuristic value of the history of science, that is, its value in helping scientists to make new discoveries, but whatever such value it may and does possess, it is clearly the trained logician rather than the pure historian who will bring it out for us, and this may well become the most valuable part of his work. He it is who should analyze for us the logic and psychology of inventions, their concatenations, their influences of all kinds upon one another. This has not yet been done with sufficient thoroughness and on a sufficiently broad basis so that we may judge whether this approach is as fruitful as it may seem, but the effort is worth

[1] Wilhelm Ostwald went so far as to say that the history of science is nothing but a method of research for the increase of scientific conquests. See his paper "La science et l'histoire des sciences" in *Revue du mois*, vol. 9, pp. 513–525 (1910).

making. The results are bound to be very interesting, even
if they do not turn out to be as immediately profitable as
one might wish. It will never be possible to replace by
systematic deductions, or by mechanical applications of old
tricks to new problems, the happy intuitions out of which
discoveries are born, but the intuitions may be guided and
stimulated by such means, and genius itself may be enabled
to soar from a higher level and with greater assurance.

* * *

I have already alluded to the psychology of scientific discovery, for, in practice, it is hardly possible to separate psychology from individual logic. However, in contrast to the
logically-minded historian, there is one who might be called
psychologically-minded, who is interested not only in the
genesis of discovery in the individual mind, but in the whole
intellectual and emotional make-up of the scientist. How
does this scientist compare with another, as a man, or with
other men? How was his temper affected by work, rest or
play, by success or failure? How was he influenced by his
social environment, and how did he influence it? How did
he express and reveal himself, or fail to reveal himself?
What was the quality of his spirit? His love of truth, his love
of beauty, his love of justice, his religion, to what extent
were they developed? Or was he indifferent to the world
around him, blind to everything except the narrow field of
his research? Not only the psychologist but the humanist
tries to answer such questions, and others innumerable.

Is this not natural enough? We have some degree of interest in every man and woman whom we approach near
enough. Should we not be even more interested in those
men who accomplished more fully the destiny of the race?
I read this morning in the paper that a man called John
O'Brien died suddenly in Boston while he was watching a
wrestling match. I have no interest whatever in wrestling,

and yet that event shocked me and aroused my curiosity. What did he die of? His was probably a heart case, and the wrestling excited him overmuch. I have no trouble in understanding that, and my sympathy goes out to him, for I have been deeply moved time after time while I was contemplating my fellow men wrestling not with other men but with nature herself, trying to solve her mysteries, to decode her messages. I have been excited by their tragic failures as much as by their occasional victories and triumphs. The same instinct which causes sport-lovers to be insatiably curious about their heroes causes the scientific humanist to ask one question after another about the great men to whom he owes his heritage of knowledge and culture. In order to satisfy that sound instinct it will be necessary to prepare detailed and reliable biographies of the men who distinguished themselves in the search for truth.

Such biographies are interesting not only in themselves, but as materials for the study of man. There is as much variety among scientists as among other people high and low. Their motives may range along the whole gamut from utter selfishness to utter selflessness, and along the whole gamut of every other passion. Their manners and customs, their temperamental reactions, differ exceedingly and introduce infinite caprice and fantasy into the development of science. The logician may frown but the humanist chuckles.

Happily such differences are more favorable to the progress of science than unfavorable. Even as all kinds of men are needed to build up a pleasant or an unpleasant community, even so we need all kinds of scientists to develop science in every possible direction. Some are very sharp and narrow-minded, others broad-minded and superficial. Many scientists, like Hannibal, know how to conquer, but not how to use their victories. Others are colonizers rather than explorers. Others are pedagogues. Others want to measure everything more accurately than it was measured before. This may lead them to the making of fundamental discoveries, or they may fail, and be looked upon as insufferable pedants. This list might be lengthened endlessly.

From the humanistic point of view, every detail in a scientist's life is or may be interesting, because that life is one of the parts in a great tragedy — we might call it the basic tragedy of mankind —, the struggle for knowledge. From that standpoint, it will never suffice to state a man's discovery; one must explain how and why he made it, and why it was he who made it, what idiosyncrasies guided or handicapped him, and so forth. Every human aspect must be considered, because this is not simply a scientific matter but a human one. One must examine his whole behavior, his ways of searching, of finding, of checking and rechecking, and finally — most illuminating of all information — his ways of expressing himself, in short, his style. "Le style, c'est l'homme."

Moreover, one cannot judge him fairly unless one is prepared to consider his achievement not only from the point of view of modern science, but also from the point of view of the knowledge obtaining in his time, and of his own education and experience. He must be seen in his own environment, and also outside of it. We must try to weigh how much he may have been helped or hindered by all kinds of social influences, most of them irrational or at least non-scientific.

To understand fully the human side of science, we must think of scientific achievements as we do of artistic achievements. Indeed they are, at best, of the same kind, though the techniques are of course very different, and even more so the intellectual attitudes. To be sure, in the scientific field even more than in the artistic one, there is a great deal of work which is so commonplace and repetitious that even a saint could hardly lift it up to an inspired level; there cannot but be many 'hewers of wood and drawers of water,' but between these and the great leaders there is an infinity of steps. Discoveries are to be judged not only in abstract terms but in human ones. The first great extension of our universe by Herschel was more startling and more moving than the periodic extensions about which we read in the daily papers ever and anon and which we have gradually come to expect.

The fundamental distinction between scientific efforts, for the humanist, is that some are heroic while others are not. That distinction cuts across all the others; it is independent of scientific value, of method, even of morality. Some men of science have cheered the whole world with their heroism, while others have done greater things, but in a smaller way, without grace and without beauty. We cannot exaggerate the significance of heroic efforts in the field of science, just as in every other field wherein men compete, for these efforts are the salt of life. If the historian keeps his eyes and his heart open for heroism, it will be easier for him to discount the false values created by success, I mean, the kind of success which is bestowed by a public opinion as fickle as it is uncritical. The record of such success (or failure) may have some social interest, but otherwise it is almost irrelevant, for what matters above all is what a man did and was, not what his contemporaries thought of him. Not all their praise, and all the honors heaped upon him, could add an inch to his stature; nor could their disapproval, neglect, and contempt subtract an inch from it. It is the historian's sacred duty to correct in the light of experience the vagaries of contemporary opinion, and to try to replace blind prejudice with well informed equity. It is his duty to reveal the motives and circumstances which cause one man to be great in spite of his failure, and another to be small in spite of his success. It is perhaps less important to point out the vanity, meddlesomeness, or cupidity of one man, than the generosity, humility, and equanimity of another; in other words, it is more useful to insist upon the good qualities of men, when we find them, than upon their shortcomings, but above all we must celebrate heroism whenever we come across it. The heroic scientist adds to the grandeur and beauty of every man's existence; the complacent, humdrum, commonplace scientist, and the meretricious, or simply the tepid, however startling his discoveries may happen to be, does not inspire us humanists and artists, but leaves us very much where we were. We may perhaps overlook him in our account, though not his discoveries, while the hero's life is in itself an artistic creation, an inexhaustible source of joy and happiness.

* * *

The history of science was and should be written from the many standpoints which I have indicated, and perhaps from still others. It is an immense subject which cannot be contemplated and illuminated from too many angles; each particular survey will add something to our knowledge and to our pleasure. Whichever the historian's point of view, he will not deserve the esteem of his colleagues if he does not do his task honestly, and, within the limits of his purpose, as completely as he can.

Such a remark might seem superfluous. It would certainly be so if we were dealing with other subjects. In fact, it would be almost impertinent to say to a zoölogist that he must do his work as honestly and thoroughly as possible, in order that others should not be obliged to do it again! Yet it is very necessary to say that very thing to the scientist who has historical investigations in view, for he seldom realizes that his own scientific methods and standards apply as rigorously to such investigations as to his own. On the contrary, he is likely to consider his historical interlude as an escapade, of which he is at one and the same time proud, because, being out of his element and having thrown his own standards to the winds, he has no others, and ashamed, because he is consciously or unconsciously aware of doing something wrong. This last feeling may lead him to make fun of his own efforts and play the clown, all of which is futile and painful to behold.

Let us repeat once more that the genuine historian (as opposed to the journalist, the hack, or the clown) should proceed exactly as every other scientist. He must determine as accurately as possible the knowledge already available on the topics he is intending to investigate; carry on his investigations with precision and thoroughness, making full use of the requisite methods and taking every precaution to avoid the various pitfalls; and, finally, publish his results in a straightforward manner. This does not mean that his account should be ugly or dull. It should be as well written as possible, but without irrelevancies or incongruous ornaments.

Whatever their task and purpose, the honest scientist and the honest historian try to accomplish it with some finality. They are ready to take endless pains in order that their efforts need not be repeated, but that the results may, on the contrary, be used by their successors as a starting point for new efforts. Thus is the progress of science made possible.

Most of the historical work done by scientists untrained as historians is published without means of verification, that is, with insufficient or imperfect references, and with so little accuracy that it is useless for later scholars. This or that statement may be right or not, one cannot tell; everything is spoiled by promiscuity of good and bad, and sometimes the whole is distorted by the author's fancy or whimsicality, or perhaps his very striving for artistic effect. Such work is obviously a waste of time for all concerned. It can add nothing to our knowledge. It rather debases the knowledge already available by diluting it with a mass of irrelevant and doubtful information whence it cannot readily be retrieved. It is truly a degradation of intellectual energy.

The ambition of the historian, like that of every other

scientist, is to increase or improve available knowledge. There is no reason for hurry, but pains should be taken to prevent slipping back, or else our work becomes hopeless. We must exert ourselves to the utmost in order that our successors may accomplish their task with greater ease and precision, and come closer to the truth than we can. Poincaré elaborated his *Méthodes nouvelles de mécanique céleste* [1] because the approximation sufficient in his day for the computations of astronomers would be no longer sufficient a few centuries later, and he once declared,[2] "We are sometimes happier to think that we have saved a day's work to our grandchildren than an hour to our contemporaries." That is the true spirit: no pains are grudged if they bring us nearer to the goal, however distant it may be. We are not in a hurry, but we must go steadily forward, not backward.

One might apply to historical work, and more particularly to our own researches, where such advice is more needed than anywhere else, the wise remarks of Albert Bayet: [3]

On conçoit maintenant la signification morale de toutes ces règles minutieuses qui président au travail scientifique. Si le savant s'impose à lui-même tant de précautions rigoureuses, c'est qu'il n'entend pas seulement atteindre la vérité: il veut la rendre manifeste à tous. Il ne lui suffit pas d'être cru: il entend ne l'être que sur preuves sonnantes et trébuchantes. Ces démonstrations exactes, ces vérifications laborieuses dont s'impatiente parfois l'esprit de finesse ou l'esprit poétique, sont la forme la plus haute de l'altruisme: elles impliquent et le désir de s'accorder avec autrui sur les choses essentielles et le désir que cet accord ne soit pas un accord de surprise, un rapprochement passager, mais bien l'expression solide d'une communauté réelle. Le respect et l'amour de l'homme pour l'homme sont l'âme de la recherche scientifique, parce qu'on ne peut pas faire aux autres un don plus précieux que de leur offrir une vérité qu'ils feront leur et qui les fera s'unir par ce qu'il y a en eux de plus haut.

---

[1] See vol. 1 (1892), introduction.
[2] *Science et méthode*, p. 34.
[3] *La morale de la science* (Paris, 1931, pp. 65–66; cf. *Isis*, vol. 19, pp. 241–245).

Alas! It is not enough for the historian to eradicate errors, he must prevent their recurrence. It happens but too often that they are reintroduced by men of science, who use the prestige honestly obtained in another domain for the unconscious dissemination of errors in our own. What would you think of the husbandman who would spare no trouble to root out weeds in his own fields, and would then sow them in the fields of his neighbors? That is exactly what has been done, and continues to be done, by very distinguished scientists. If the movement which I am leading had no other result but to prevent that especially ugly kind of carelessness and selfishness, and to put an end to the degenerescence of historical truth caused by it, I should already feel well repaid for my labor.

* * *

Many techniques are involved in our investigations, not only the ordinary scientific and historical techniques, but others less usual and more absorbing, if not more difficult. For example, the historian of mediaeval science, that is, he who wishes to make a comparative survey of science and learning in the Middle Ages, must be prepared to study Arabic, as a great many scientific books were written in that language. That knowledge of an Oriental language which would be somewhat of a luxury for other mediaevalists is almost a necessity for him, a necessity which entails a vast amount of work.

The study of an additional and difficult technique, such as that of palaeography or an Oriental language, is an excellent training for any scholar. It gives him the exhilarating feeling of coming closer to rare sources and being able to drink from them; it creates in him a sense of independence and mastery; it ought to lift him high above the temptations of clap-trap and irresponsible historical writing. Just as we should have less confidence in a professor of general physics who had not mastered any of the special techniques of physical research, just so we are less inclined to trust a historian of science who is too much of a theorist and who has not experienced time after time the tribulations of defeat and the joys of victory in the digging out of facts from the bed rock.

Every historian must be trained to overcome certain classes of technical difficulties, and, in a way, the harder these are, the better. Nevertheless it is well to remember that this training introduces new perils. It is possible to teach the most difficult techniques and the most esoteric methods to people of mediocre intelligence, but it is impossible to impart to them the wisdom which is needed to make the best of any technique and to master it truly, instead of being mastered by it. In too many cases the technique ceases to be a means to an end, but becomes an end in itself, and that is very silly.

At the end of their excellent textbook on statistics, Professor Harold T. Davis and W. F. C. Nelson give the following warning, which fits my argument as well as their own.[1] When the student has mastered a definite technique, what then?

The danger [say Davis and Nelson] is that he will over-estimate rather than under-estimate the value of this equipment. Statistical methodology is no magical, or even mechanical, instrument that automatically grinds out valid conclusions and allows the suspension or avoidance of personal judgment. Indeed, it may be said flatly that a statistical conclusion is no better than the judgment of the statistician who produced it. Knowing what tool to employ is just as important as knowing how to employ it. The second can be taught, but the first must be learned. The novice will tend to think that the more high-powered his methods the more cogent his analysis. This is not at all necessarily true. A scatter diagram may well yield more information than a correlation coefficient. The fact that the latter may be carried to several decimal

---

[1] *Elements of Statistics* (Bloomington, Indiana, 1935), p. 334; cf. *Isis*, vol. 25, p. 279. My reference to a book on statistics is not so arbitrary as it may seem. See my "Quetelet," in *Isis*, vol. 23, pp. 6–24 (1935).

places gives a spurious appearance of accuracy, while it may really be concealing such facts as that the relationship is curvilinear or that some of the observations are evidently grossly distorted. In such a case, the apparently crude method is really enlightening, the apparently precise method is really deceptive. Very often a free hand curve drawn through a graph will tell as much about the trend as will ever be revealed by logistics or quintics. Again, the methods may be too refined for the data.

Much intellectual mediocrity can be and actually is concealed by some technique sufficiently recondite to discourage outside criticism, even as social conventions can easily mask the lack of individuality, or religious rites provide the best of screens for moral unfitness, and even for iniquity.

This is as true for science as for history. It is pathetic to think of the efforts made in hundreds of laboratories to realize with the most complicated and forbidding apparatus the most futile experiments.

Parturiunt montes, nascetur ridiculus mus.

The danger of pedantry and of unbalanced technicality will always be with us, because mediocrity is far more common than intelligence, not to speak of genius, and because the number of fools is always large. Moreover, it is well-nigh impossible to say where pedantry begins. We hardly dare interfere with the excessively complicated experiments of an unwise scientist, because it is impossible to appreciate the situation with fairness without identifying ourselves, as it were, with him. We may suspect that his experiments will be futile, but we are not sufficiently sure of it to stop him. Pedantry cannot be inferred from the subject. A man may spend his life compiling a dictionary or a mathematical table and yet not be a pedant; or he may seem to be very catholic in his tastes and yet be a pedant at heart; some of the worst of the tribe are found among self-styled poets and artists.

The fundamental difference between creative scholarship and pedantry lies in the power of selection which wise men have and pedants lack. Now this brings science and art very close together, for right selection is the essence of art as well as of science.

The artist cannot reproduce every aspect of nature or realize every dream of his mind; he must choose, choose, choose. Even so the scientist cannot study every fact and attack every problem; he must choose and choose and choose again. His activities are continually dominated by the need of selection; they may be suddenly exalted by a wise choice, or jeopardized, even nullified, by a wrong one. Genius in science as well as in art includes, as one of its essential elements, that uncanny quality, the ability to select the most characteristic lines or colors, melodies, or harmonies, or the salient fact, the fertile problem, the 'crucial' or enlightening experiment. Granted that selection is even more fundamentally and continually important for the artist than for the scientist,[1] that is, that artistic creation is far more arbitrary than scientific creation, the difference between them is quantitative rather than, as is generally believed, qualitative.

We must try to impart difficult techniques and rigorous methods without making pedants. It is true the problem is largely solved for us before we try to solve it ourselves, for some men are born pedants, and whatever technical skill is given to them will only feed their pedantry; just as some people are born hypocrites, and religious training can only make them worse. However, it is well to know the dangers

---

[1] Einstein once remarked that the infinitesimal calculus would certainly have been discovered even if there had been no Newton and no Leibniz, but without Beethoven we should never have had a C minor symphony. Alexander Moszkowski, *Einstein the Searcher* (London, 1921), p. 99. That is incontrovertible. Yet one may object, on the one hand, that the arbitrariness of scientific creation can be very well illustrated by Einstein's own example, the early history of the calculus; on the other hand, that the development of the symphony would have continued after Mozart, even if there had been no Beethoven. It remains true that Beethoven's work is absolutely individual and as such irreplaceable, while Newton's would have been replaced sooner or later by something equivalent.

at our right and at our left; this will help us to avoid them, if it be at all in our power to do so.

Bearing in mind these limitations, the study of the history of science will give scholars abundant fruits, and over and above that, it will give more wisdom to the wise, more human sympathy to those who are capable of it, and, to those whose souls are open to admiration rather than cynicism, new opportunities of admiring some of the greatest achievements of mankind.

BIBLIOGRAPHY

BIBLIOGRAPHY

This list, prepared for the beginner, will enable him, short as it is, to continue his bibliographical preparation to any extent. It is divided into seven sections:

I. Historical methods.

II. Scientific methods.

III. Chief reference books for the history of science. A. History and biography; B. Catalogues of scientific literature; C. Union lists of scientific periodicals; D. General scientific journals.

IV. Journals and serials on the history of science.

V. Treatises on the history of science.

VI. Handbooks on the history of science.

VII. Societies and congresses. A. History of science societies; B. National scientific societies; C. International congresses.

It should be noted that the history of each science has its own bibliography, and that all these bibliographies are somewhat overlapping. I propose to deal with the history of separate sciences on other occasions; meanwhile an intelligent student would have no insurmountable difficulties in compiling a special bibliography of the history of any science (or any subject) on the basis of the indications given below.

I. Historical Methods

The best known of treatises on historical methods are:

Ernst Bernheim (1850–   ), *Lehrbuch der historischen Methode* (Leipzig, 1889; often reprinted).

Charles Victor Langlois (1863–1929) and Charles Seignobos (1854–   ), *Introduction aux études historiques* (Paris, 1897; often reprinted).

I have never used Bernheim. The book of Langlois and Seignobos is excellent; it has been translated into English by G. G. Berry (London, 1898; reprinted in 1912, 1925, 1926).

Ch. V. Langlois, *Manuel de bibliographie historique* (Paris, 1901–04).

Louis John Paetow (1880–1928), *A Guide to the Study of Medieval History* (Berkeley, 1917). Revised edition prepared by the Mediaeval Academy of America (New York, 1931). A very useful book and not only for the mediaevalist.

By means of Langlois's books and Paetow's it is possible to explore the main historical literature, and become acquainted with historical methods in general.

For the general point of view of the historian of science, see G. Sarton, *The History of Science and the New Humanism* (New York, 1931; cf. *Isis*, vol. 16, pp. 451-455); Federigo Enriques, *Signification de l'histoire de la pensée scientifique* (Paris, 1934; 68 pp.; cf. *Isis*, vol. 23, p. 576); Abel Rey, *Les mathématiques en Grèce au milieu du V siècle* (Paris, 1935; 92 pp.; generalities at the beginning; cf. *Isis*, vol. 24, p. 470).

II. Scientific Methods

The only way to study scientific methods thoroughly is to work in a special field of science, and to carry on as many experiments and investigations as possible. Book knowledge cannot possibly replace the experimental knowledge obtained in the laboratory. Of course this is true also of historical methods, which can only be mastered by long practice.

However, for the historian of science, the experimental knowledge, indispensable as it is, is not sufficient. He must be more fully aware of the methods which scientists are applying to their purpose, and be able to analyze them.

There are a great many books dealing with the methods of science, and I could not tell which are the best, as I have read only a few. A good part of that subject is already standardized, and explained sufficiently well in every book.

Karl Pearson (1857-1936), *The Grammar of Science* (London, 1892; often reprinted). A pioneer work, still valuable.

Federigo Enriques, *Problemi della scienza* (Bologna, 1906). French translation (1909), German translation (1910), second Italian edition (1910), English translation entitled *Problems of Science* (Chicago, 1914; cf. *Isis*, vol. 3, p. 368). The author is a mathematician and the head of the institute for the history of science attached to the University of Rome.

Henri Poincaré (1854-1912), *La science et l'hypothèse* (Paris, 1908); *La valeur de la science* (1909); *Science et méthode* (1909). These books have been often reprinted and translated into many languages. The English translation of them by George Bruce Halsted with a special preface by the author and an introduction by Josiah Royce is available in a single volume (New York, 1913; many times reprinted).

Frederic William Westaway, *Scientific Method: Its Philosophical Basis and its Modes of Application* (London, 1912, later editions 1919, 1924, 1931; cf. *Isis*, vol. 4, pp. 119-122). On a much lower level than the preceding books, and thus more accessible to the average student. The author is an inspector of the English schools.

Arthur David Ritchie, *Scientific Method. An Inquiry into the Character and Validity of Natural Laws* (London, 1923). The author is a chemical physiologist.

André Lamouche, *La méthode générale des sciences pures et appliquées* (Paris, 1924). The author is an engineer in the French navy.

Abraham Wolf, *Essentials of Scientific Method* (London, 1925). Many times reprinted. The author is professor of the subject in the University of London, and he is also a historian of science.

Alfred North Whitehead, *Science and the Modern World* (Cambridge, 1926). The author is a mathematician and metaphysician.

Frederick Barry, *The Scientific Habit of Thought. An Informal Discussion of the Source and Character of Dependable Knowledge* (New York, 1927; cf. *Isis*, vol. 14, pp. 265–268). The author is a chemist, now professor of the history of science in Columbia University.

Norman Robert Campbell, *Physics, the Elements* (London, 1920); *An Account of the Principles of Measurement and Calculation* (London, 1928). The author is a physicist.

Harold T. Davis, *Philosophy and Modern Science* (Bloomington, Indiana, 1931; cf. *Isis*, vol. 18, pp. 204–206). The author is a mathematician and statistician.

Every student of the history of science should read at least Poincaré's immortal books, but that would not suffice. Poincaré's books are collections of essays, which do not replace more systematic treatises. With regard to the other books mentioned above, I will add two remarks.

1. Though these books have many elements in common, they are very different in contents and in spirit, and answer different purposes. Students need not read them all, but only a few; they should examine them and select those which seem the best for their own needs. They must be made to realize the concreteness of scientific methods and also their philosophical implications.

2. The list is exemplary rather than exhaustive. I have mentioned some of the books I have come across; there are many others with which I am not familiar and which may be as good, if not better.

III. Chief Reference Books for the History of Science

A. *History and Biography*

George Sarton, *Introduction to the History of Science*. Vol. 1. From Homer to Omar Khayyam (Baltimore, 1927). Vol. 2, in two parts. From Rabbi ben Ezra to Roger Bacon (1931). Vol. 3. Science and Learning in the Fourteenth Century (in preparation).

Ludwig Darmstaedter (1846–1927), *Handbuch zur Geschichte der Naturwissenschaften und der Technik*. Zweite Auflage (Berlin, 1908). Chronological list of discoveries year by year. Valuable, but to be used with caution.

August Hirsch (1817–94), *Biographisches Lexikon der hervorragenden Ärzte aller Zeiten und Völker* (1884–88, 6 vols.). New edition prepared by W. Haberling, F. Hübotter, and H. Vierordt (Berlin, 1929–34, 5 vols.; supplement, 1935).

I. Fischer, *Biographisches Lexikon der hervorragenden Ärzte der letzten fünfzig Jahren* (Berlin, 1932–33, 2 vols.).

These dictionaries of medical biography supplement Poggendorff's work, which is restricted to the exact sciences, and the more so because they contain biographies of many naturalists; indeed, down to the nineteenth century the majority of these were physicians.

Aksel G. S. Josephson, *A List of Books on the History of Science*. January, 1911. Supplement, December, 1916 (John Crerar Library, Chicago, 1911–17). Though this is only a library catalogue, and is already twenty years old, it is still a valuable tool, the authors' names and titles of books being quoted with great accuracy.

B. *Catalogues of Scientific Literature*

Johann Christian Poggendorff (1796–1877), *Biographisch literarisches Handwörterbuch zur Geschichte der exakten Wissenschaften* (Leipzig, 1863, 2 vols.). Vol. 3 for the period 1858–83 (1898). Vol. 4 for the period 1883–1904 (1904). Vol. 5 for the period 1904–22 (1926).

Royal Society of London, *Catalogue of Scientific Papers, 1800–1900* (Cambridge, 1867–1925, 19 vols.). Subject index (1908–14, 4 vols.).

This work is so important that we must pause a moment to describe it. Its compilation was first suggested at the Glasgow meeting of the B.A.A.S. in 1855 by Joseph Henry (1797–1878), secretary of the Smithsonian Institution, and the plan was drawn up in 1857. After many years of preparation and considerable expenditure, the first volume appeared in 1867, and the publication continued as follows:

First series. Vols. i–vi, cataloguing the papers of 1800–63, 1867–77.

Second series. Vols. vii–viii, literature of 1864–73, 1877–79.

Third series. Vols. ix–xi, literature of 1874–83, 1891–96.

Vol. xii. Supplement to the previous volumes, 1902.

Fourth series. Vols. xiii–xix, literature of 1884–1900, 1914–25.

To give an idea of the size of this catalogue it will suffice to remark that the papers catalogued in the fourth series alone, for the period 1884–1900, number 384,478, by 68,577 authors.

The compilation of a subject index, without which the work loses much of its value, was already contemplated in the first plan (1857). It was finally decided to arrange it in accordance with the *International Catalogue of Scientific Literature* (see below). This meant that it would include seventeen volumes, one for each of the seventeen sciences recognized in that catalogue. The first volume, Pure Mathematics, appeared in 1908; the second, Mechanics, in 1909, the third, Physics, in two instalments, Generalities, Heat, Light, Sound in 1912, Electricity and Magnetism in 1914. The publication seems to have been finally discontinued, which is a great pity. Whatever the fate of the International Catalogue may be, there is no justification for leaving the Royal Society Catalogue essentially incomplete, and thus nullifying a large part of the past labor and expenditure.

International Catalogue of Scientific Literature. Published for the International Council by the Royal Society of London.

This is an outgrowth of the Royal Society Catalogue, as it was felt that the scientific literature of our century was too extensive to be dealt with by a single scientific society. Its organization was arranged at the initiative of the Royal Society, by an international conference which met in London in 1896, then again in 1898, in 1900, etc. It was decided to divide science into seventeen branches:

A. Mathematics.
B. Mechanics.
C. Physics.
D. Chemistry.
E. Astronomy.
F. Meteorology (incl. Terrestrial magnetism).
G. Mineralogy (incl. Petrology and Crystallography).
H. Geology.
J. Geography (mathematical and physical).
K. Palaeontology.
L. General biology.
M. Botany.
N. Zoology.
O. Human anatomy.
P. Physical anthropology.
Q. Physiology (incl. experimental Psychology, Pharmacology, and experimental Pathology).
R. Bacteriology.

A large number of volumes were actually published from 1902 to 1916, but the gigantic undertaking was a victim of the World War and of the national selfishness and loss of idealism which the War induced. The volumes published cover the scientific literature for the period from 1901 to about 1913.[1]

---

[1] The publication includes 254 octavo volumes, varying in thickness from half an inch to two inches, and the original price was about £260. The stock has been sold to William Dawson and Sons, London, who offer a complete set for the price of £60 unbound, or £100 bound (November, 1935).

C. *Union Lists of Scientific Periodicals*

The two most important lists of that kind are:

1. The *Union List of Serials in Libraries of the United States and Canada* (New York, 1927, one very large quarto volume of 1588 pp.).

Registering some 70,000 journals and serials, of every kind, dead or alive, published in some 70 languages, and available in some 225 American libraries. Two supplements have already appeared, bringing the list down to 1932.

2. *A World List of Scientific Periodicals Published in the Years 1900–1933*. Second edition (London, 1934, large quarto, 794 pp.). Less comprehensive than 1 because it is restricted to contemporary scientific publications, it includes some 36,000 entries in 18 languages (for statistics, see *Isis*, vol. 23, p. 578).

These two lists are useful, first, to identify a certain journal, secondly, to find in what libraries (British or American) sets of it are available, and, finally, to judge of its importance, or at least of its popularity, by the number of sets available in the English-speaking world. This last judgment is possible only in the case of publications which are not distributed mostly by gift or exchange.

D. *General Scientific Journals*

For the study of science and the determination of the main impulses and tendencies of contemporary research, it is well to consult journals devoted to science in general. The ten leading journals of that kind are, in chronological order:

1. *Revue scientifique*. Paris, 1863.
2. *Nature*. London, 1869.
3. *La Nature*. Paris, 1873.
4. *Science*. New York, 1883.
5. *Naturwissenschaftliche Rundschau*. Braunschweig, 1886–1912.
6. *Revue générale des sciences pures et appliquées*. Paris, 1890.
7. *Science Progress in the Twentieth Century*. London, 1906.
8. *Scientia*. Bologna, 1907.
9. *Die Naturwissenschaften*. Berlin, 1913. (A continuation of 5.)
10. *Discovery*. London, 1920.

The richest in information of these journals is *Nature*. It contains by far the largest collection of material of this sort; by the end of 1935, 136 large volumes had been published. Each volume is indexed, but there are no general indices.

Of these journals the only ones having general indices are the *Revue scientifique* for the period 1863–81, *La Nature* for 1873–1912 (four decennial indices), the *Revue générale des sciences* for 1890–1914, and *Die Naturwissenschaften* for 1913–27. Thus through these four journals the general scientific achievements of the period 1863–1927 are indexed to some degree.

IV. Journals and Serials on the History of Science

The chief journals and serials are quoted in chronological order. The publishers named are in each case the latest or last.

1. *Klassiker der exakten Naturwissenschaften.* Founded by Wilhelm Ostwald (1853–1932). (Leipzig, 1889, etc.) Vols. 238, 239 appeared in 1934. Publisher, Akademische Verlagsgesellschaft, Leipzig.

2. *Mitteilungen zur Geschichte der Medizin und der Naturwissenschaften, herausgegeben von der Deutschen Gesellschaft für Geschichte der Medizin und der Naturwissenschaften* (vol. 1, 1902; in 1936, vol. 35 is being published). Almost exclusively bibliographical. Publisher, Leopold Voss, Leipzig.

3. *Archiv für die Geschichte der Naturwissenschaften und der Technik* (13 vols. published from 1909 to 1930; vol. 9 contains only 126 pp.). Publisher, F. C. W. Vogel, Leipzig.

4. *Rivista di storia critica delle scienze mediche e naturali* (vol. 1, 1910). Organ of the Italian Society for the History of Science. Direttore: Andrea Corsini, Via de' Bardi 5, Firenze (113).

5. *Isis.* Quarterly organ of the History of Science Society and bibliographical organ of the International Academy for the History of Science. Edited by George Sarton (vol. 1, 1913; the publication of vol. 26 began in 1936). Publisher, Saint Catherine Press, Bruges.

This is the chief journal devoted to the history of science and the most comprehensive. It includes new contributions, reviews, notes, abundant illustrations, and a very elaborate critical bibliography covering the whole field. That bibliography is arranged in the same order as Sarton's *Introduction*; it corrects and keeps up to date the volumes of the *Introduction* already published and accumulates materials in their proper sequence for the ulterior volumes.

6. *Studies in the History and Method of Science.* Edited by Charles Singer (1917–21, 2 vols. quarto, with illustrations). Published by the Clarendon Press, Oxford.

A splendid collection, unfortunately interrupted after the second volume.

7. *Archivio di storia della scienza*, later called *Archeion*. Edited by Aldo Mieli (vol. 1, 1919; in 1935, vol. 17 is being published; vol. 10 has never been completed). Official organ of the International Academy of the

History of Science, 12 rue Colbert, Paris II. Published by the Casa Editrice Leonardo da Vinci, Rome.

8. *Abhandlungen zur Geschichte der Naturwissenschaften und der Medizin.* Edited by Oskar Schulz (7 parts published, numbered 1 to 2 and 4 to 8. 1922–25). Publisher, Max Mencke, Erlangen, Bavaria.

9. *Quellen und Studien zur Geschichte der Mathematik, Astronomie, und Physik.* Edited by O. Neugebauer, J. Stenzel, and O. Toeplitz. Published in two sections, A, Quellen, and B, Studien. Section A began to appear in 1930 and section B in 1931.

10. *Quellen und Studien zur Geschichte der Naturwissenschaften und der Medizin.* Edited by P. Diepgen and J. Ruska. Continuation of the *Archiv* (no. 3). Began to appear in 1931. Nos. 9 and 10, complementing one another, are published by Julius Springer, Berlin.

11. *Archives for the History of Science and Technology* (in Russian). Published in Leningrad by the Academy of Sciences of the USSR (first volume, 1933, eighth volume, 1936). Regularly analyzed in *Isis* like all other periodicals, sometimes at greater length, as relatively few non-Russians are able to read Russian.

12. *Abhandlungen zur Geschichte der Medizin und Naturwissenschaften.* Edited by Paul Diepgen, Julius Ruska, and Julius Schuster (Heft 1, Berlin, 1934; Heft 8, 1935). Verlag Dr. Emil Ebering, Berlin.

13. *Thalès. Recueil annuel des travaux de l'Institut d'histoire des sciences et des techniques de l'Université de Paris.* Première année, 1934. Published by Alcan, Paris, in 1935. Edited by Abel Rey, Ducassé, Pierre Brunet.

14. *Osiris.* Studies on the History and Philosophy of Science, and on the History of Learning and Culture. Edited by George Sarton (vol. 1, Bruges, 1936).

This series is supplementary to *Isis.* It will include volumes devoted to a single subject or group of subjects (as vol. 1, devoted to the history of mathematics) and the longer and more technical papers; *Isis,* the shorter ones, the reviews, notes, queries, and critical bibliography.

15. *Annals of Science. A Quarterly Review for the History of Science since the Renaissance.* Edited by Douglas McKie, Harcourt Brown, and H. W. Robinson (London, 1936). Publishers, Taylor and Francis, London E.C. 4.

There are many more journals and serials devoted to the history of special sciences, especially the medical ones, but they can all be traced through the bibliographies above mentioned. In 1914, Sarton published a list of sixty-two reviews and collections devoted to the history of science (*Isis,* vol. 2, pp. 125–161); many other items could now easily be added to it through the critical bibliographies published in *Isis* ever since (no. 45 in vol. 25). Indeed, these bibliographies constitute a systematic and continuous table of contents to all the reviews and serials dealing with the history and philosophy of science, and to all the similar materials published in other journals or anywhere.[1]

Journals devoted to the history of science contain many articles on the philosophy of science, these two groups of subjects being closely related. Articles on the philosophy of science are also found in most philosophical journals. For example, the *Revue de métaphysique et de morale*, founded in 1893, by Xavier Léon (1868–1935) and edited by him (general tables for vols. 1 to 30, 1893–1923), has published a magnificent series of papers on the subject, including many of Poincaré's. A special journal, *Philosophy of Science*, edited by William Marias Malisoff, has been published by Williams and Wilkins in Baltimore since 1934.

V. TREATISES ON THE HISTORY OF SCIENCE

The earliest treatise deserving to be quoted here is William Whewell, *History of the Inductive Sciences from the Earliest to the Present Times* (London, 1837, 3 vols.). Vol. 1 deals with Greek physics, Greek astronomy, mediaeval physics, and astronomy from Copernicus to Kepler; vol. 2, with the history of mechanics, physical astronomy, acoustics, optics, "thermotics and atmology"; vol. 3, with other branches of physics, chemistry, natural history, physiology and comparative anatomy, and, finally, geology. Irrespective of its many shortcomings, some of which were unavoidable a century ago, this book is not a history of science as we understand it to-day, but a juxtaposition of various special histories, which is something very different; it represents a lower stage of integration.

Thus far there is only one modern complete treatise on the history of science. That is Friedrich Dannemann, *Die Naturwissenschaften in ihrer Entwicklung und in ihrem Zusammenhange* (Leipzig, 1910–13, 4 vols.; 2d ed. 1920–23; cf. *Isis*, vol. 2, pp. 218–222; vol. 4, pp. 110, 563; vol. 6, p. 115). It is elementary and imperfect, yet Dannemann, like Whewell, was a pioneer, and deserves our gratitude on that account.

When one remembers, on the one hand, the insufficiency of this treatise, and on the other hand, that it is not only the best but the only one of its kind, one realizes more keenly the immaturity of our studies and the immensity of the task to be accomplished.

Three new treatises have been begun but are only incompletely published:

Abel Rey, *La science dans l'antiquité* (Paris, 1930–33). This is a part of Henri Berr's collection *L'évolution de l'humanité*. Two volumes have appeared: vol. 1, La science orientale avant les Grecs; vol 2, La jeunesse de la science grecque (cf. *Isis*, vol. 21, pp. 224–226).

[1] As far as available to the editor of *Isis*.

Federigo Enriques and G. de Santillana, *Storia del pensiero scientifico*, vol. 1, Il mondo antico (Milano, 1932; cf. *Isis*, vol. 23, pp. 467–469).

Pierre Brunet and Aldo Mieli, *Histoire des sciences*. Antiquité (Paris, 1935; cf. *Isis*, vol. 24, pp. 444–447).

Of these three works the first is built on by far the largest scale, and is the most erudite. The two volumes thus far published by Rey carry the story only down to the middle of the fifth century B.C. Each of the two other works covers the whole of antiquity and the beginning of the Middle Ages in a single volume. Enriques's treatise is more philosophical; Brunet and Mieli's more elaborate. Moreover, the latter is a combination between a treatise and an anthology, about half of the space being sacrificed to a collection of extracts from the original writings in French translation. Further comparisons between these three works would be invidious.

To these books must be added one of a different kind, which is in a class by itself.

Lynn Thorndike, *A History of Magic and Experimental Science during the First Thirteen Centuries of our Era* (New York, 1923, 2 vols.; cf. *Isis*, vol. 6, pp. 74–89); and *in the Fourteenth and Fifteenth Centuries* (New York, 1934, 2 more vols.; cf. *Isis*, vol. 23, pp. 471–475).

These four volumes deal largely with the borderland between science and magic. They are very erudite, and historians of science should not fail to consult them.

It is interesting to note that the authors of all these treatises are professional students of the history of science, that is, men for whom that study has become the main activity. Even the old William Whewell (1794–1866), trained as a mathematician and physicist, devoted most of his time to the history and philosophy of science. Dannemann, now retired, was for many years a teacher of the history of science. Abel Rey, by training a philosopher, is professor of our subject at the Sorbonne and director of the Institute of the History of Science attached to the University of Paris; the mathematician Enriques is now director of a similar institute in the University of Rome and Santillana is his assistant; Mieli, who learned the methods of science as a chemist, is the founder and permanent secretary of the International Academy of the History of Science in Paris, and Brunet is a collaborator of his. Thorndike has devoted his whole life to the study of the interrelations between science and magic.

VI. HANDBOOKS ON THE HISTORY OF SCIENCE

When scholars are beginning to take an interest in our studies, their first query is, naturally enough, "Could you recommend a single volume giving an outline of the whole subject?" Such a volume does not yet exist, and this is not surprising when one knows how the matter stands with regard to treatises. Elementary books can only be written in a satisfactory way when elaborate treatises are available. It is possible to-day to write a little book covering the whole of, say English literature, or the Reformation, or any other standardized subject, and to be confident that, however small the scale, nothing essential, from the standpoint of that scale, is likely to be overlooked. For the history of science such a feat of selection and compression is still impossible, because the introductory analyses and surveys have not yet been completed; or, if not impossible, it is very much of a wager and a gamble.

A few years ago the veteran historian of science Siegmund Günther wrote a little book, *Geschichte der Naturwissenschaften* (Reclam series, 1909). The degree of selection being much too small for the degree of compression, the book is unreadable: it is more like a catalogue than a story. It is as if one tried to crowd too many names on a small scale map.

The best single volume available to-day is Sir William Cecil Dampier Dampier-Whetham's *A History of Science and its Relations with Philosophy and Religion* (Cambridge, 1929; cf. *Isis*, vol. 14, pp. 263–265).

William Thompson Sedgwick (1855–1921) and Harry Walter Tyler, *A Short History of Science* (New York, 1917). A primer, which I only quote for lack of better. The surviving author, Tyler, is preparing a new edition, which will certainly be an improvement.

Charles Singer has been working on an introductory volume for many years, the *Short History of Science*, to be published soon by the Clarendon Press. Another book almost ready for publication is Benjamin Ginzburg's *Origins of Modern Science*.

If we had to select a guidebook to Europe, purporting to indicate and to explain within the covers of a single volume the chief curiosities of the whole continent, our first question would concern the personality of the author. Of course we should have more confidence in him if we knew he had himself travelled all over Europe than if we discovered that he had compiled his guide in the New York Public Library. In a similar way, for the appreciation of a handbook on the history of science, the prime consideration must be the wisdom and experience of the writer.

Siegmund Günther (1848–1923) was one of the founders of the history of science movement in Germany, and the author of many books and memoirs on the history of the mathematical and physical sciences. Sir William Cecil Dampier Dampier-Whetham is a physico-chemist, but for the last twenty-five years he has devoted much time and thought to the history and the cultural aspects of science. Sedgwick and Tyler, the first a biologist, the second a mathematician, taught the history of science for many years at the Massachusetts Institute of Technology. Charles Singer, a physician, is the leading historian of medicine and biology in the British Empire.

VII. SOCIETIES AND CONGRESSES

A. *History of Science Societies*

Academies of science and scientific societies ocasionally take an interest in the history and philosophy of science. For example, the Académie des Sciences of Paris awards every year (since 1903) a prize, the Prix Binoux, to encourage work in that field (*Isis*, vol. 8, p. 161; vol. 25, p. 136). Moreover, the older academies and societies are naturally concerned with their own glorious past, with the history of their achievements and institutions and the biographies of their members, and this has often induced them to promote historical investigations.[1] The jubilee publications of those bodies sometimes contain historical memoirs of real value, which do not always receive the publicity they deserve and thus are relatively unknown.

However, the attention paid to our studies by those societies whose main interests are different from ours is erratic, and not much assistance can be expected from them. Therefore it has been found necessary to create special societies devoted to the study of the history of science.

The five principal ones are, in chronological order:

1. 1901. Deutsche Gesellschaft für Geschichte der Medizin und der Naturwissenschaften. Founded at Hamburg, September 25, 1901, by Karl Sudhoff and others. Publishes the *Mitteilungen zur Geschichte der Medizin und der Naturwissenschaften*, 1902 ff.

Annual dues, RM.20. Address: Rudolf Blanckertz, Georgenkirchstr. 44, Berlin NO 43, Germany.

2. 1907. Società italiana di storia critica delle scienze mediche e naturali. Founded at Perugia, October 9, 1907, by Domenico Barduzzi

---

[1] Two academic undertakings deserve special mention because of their unusual amplitude and quality:

1. The reports prepared by the Institut de France by order of Napoleon on the progress of science from 1789 to 1810. J. B. J. Delambre, *Rapport historique sur les progrès des sciences mathématiques depuis 1789 et sur leur état actuel* (272 pp.). Including mechanics, astronomy, geography, arts and industries. Georges Cuvier, *Rapport historique sur les progrès des sciences naturelles* (298 pp.). Including chemistry, physics, physiology, natural history, medicine, agriculture. André Dacier, *Rapport historique sur les progrès de l'histoire et de la littérature ancienne* (263 pp.). The three quarto volumes were published at Paris in 1810.

2. The series of histories of particular sciences prepared by order of the Royal Academy of Sciences of Bavaria. A series of some 24 volumes, which began to appear about 1864 and was completed about half a century later. It is the finest series of its kind.

(1847–1929) and others. Publishes *Atti delle riunioni*, 1909 ff., and *Rivista di storia critica delle scienze mediche e naturali*, 1913 ff.

Annual dues: L.25 in Italy, L.50 abroad. Address: Prof. Andrea Corsini, Via de' Bardi 5, Firenze (113), Italy.

3. 1924. History of Science Society. Founded in Boston, January 12, 1924, by David Eugene Smith and others. Publishes *Isis* and various books; the members receive *Isis* free of charge, but not the other publications.

Annual dues: $5. Address: Frederick E. Brasch, Library of Congress, Washington, D. C., U. S. A.

4. 1928. Académie internationale d'histoire des sciences. Founded in Oslo, August 18, 1928, by Aldo Mieli and others. Its official organ is *Archeion*, and its bibliographic organ, *Isis*.

Membership restricted to a hundred elected members. Address: Perpetual secretary, Aldo Mieli, 12 rue Colbert, Paris 2, France.

5. 1935. Lärdomshistoriska Samfundet (Society of the History of Learning). Founded in Upsala in 1934 by Johan Nordström and others. Publishes Lychnos, *Lärdomshistoriska Samfundets Årsbok*, an annual review; vol. 1, 1936.

Annual dues: 8 crowns. Address: Prof. J. Nordström, University, Upsala, Sweden.

This society, the youngest of all, is also by far the largest in membership. It already counted 1750 members in May, 1935, before its publications began to appear.

Each of these societies and of others less important or devoted to a single science or group of sciences (as medicine) is a centre of research for our studies. In addition to their regular and irregular publications, they organize annual meeetings, lectures, and discussions.

B. *National Scientific Societies*

Many countries have organized annual scientific congresses, the importance of which cannot be overestimated. It is true, they do not much influence the progress of science, which is taken care of more effectively by the academies and the special scientific societies, but they are very powerful in diffusing scientific knowledge and the appreciation of scientific methods, and in moulding public opinion. The parent and model of these national associations is the Gesellschaft deutscher Naturforscher und Ärzte, which met for the first time at Leipzig in 1822, and, has met every year since, each time in a different town of Germany or Austria. The other national societies also move from town to town and thus establish each year a new centre of diffusion. The proceedings of these societies enable historians of science to determine the main trends in science year by year; moreover sections of those societies are or may be devoted to our studies.

The five main national societies are, in chronological order:

1. 1822. G.d.N.A. Gesellschaft deutscher Naturforscher und Ärzte. Unfortunately the publications are very irregular. The reports (*Verhandlungen* and other titles) of the early meetings appeared in the *Isis* of Lorenz Oken (1779–1851) who was the founder of the Gesellschaft; in 1836, the *Tageblatt der Versammlung* began to appear; since 1924 the *Mitteilungen* are published as a supplement to *Die Naturwissenschaften*. I know of no general guide or indices to all these proceedings, nor have I ever seen a complete set of them.

Offices: Gustav Adolfstr. 12, Leipzig C 1.

A section is devoted to the history of medicine and natural sciences, its meeting being organized in conjunction with the German society *ad hoc*. The proceedings of that section are generally published in the third or Dutch *Janus*,[1] one of the leading journals on the history of medicine founded in 1896 and published at Haarlem and later at Leyden.

2. 1831. B.A.A.S. British Association for the Advancement of Science. This association met for the first time at York in 1831, and has met every year since in a different town of Great Britain or the British Empire. Its influence upon the English speaking peoples has been quite considerable. Its *Reports* published annually in separate volumes since 1831, with general indices for the years 1831–60 and 1861–90, constitute a valuable collection for the historian of science (as opposed to the German reports, which being scattered and irregularly published are so difficult to consult in their entirety that one does not try to).

No special section of the B.A.A.S. is devoted to the history of science. Address: Burlington House, London, W. 1. The official residence of the Permanent Secretary is now at Down House, at Downe, Kent, formerly Darwin's home (see *Isis*, vol. 23, pp. 533, 534).

3. 1848. A.A.A.S. American Association for the Advancement of Science. *Proceedings* published in annual volumes until 1910. Since then the full proceedings appear in *Science*, and only Summarized Proceedings from time to time in book form. No indices. Section L is devoted to the 'historical and philological sciences.' The annual meetings of the History of Science Society are arranged to coincide every other year with the meetings of section L, and on the alternate years with the meetings of the American Historical Association.

Address of A.A.A.S.: Smithsonian Institution, Washington, D. C.

4. 1872. A.F.A.S. Association Française pour l'Avancement des Sciences. *Comptes-rendus*, published every year, no indices. There is no

---

[1] Two other medico-historical journals bearing the same name preceded the Dutch *Janus* (see *Isis*, vol. 2, p. 143, 146; vol. 17, pp. 283–284).

section devoted to the history of science as such, but there is an archaeological section.

Address: Secrétariat de l'Association, rue Serpente 28, Paris VI.

5. 1907. S.I.P.S. Società Italiana per il Progresso delle Scienze. *Atti*, published each year.[1] Elaborate decennial indices for 1907–19, 1921–31. Section 1 of class C deals with history and archaeology, section 2 with philology, section 5 with philosophy. Address: Via del Collegio Romano 26, Roma.

C. *International Congresses*

International congresses have been organized for almost every science or group of sciences, and one of their sections is generally devoted to historical subjects. It is not possible to deal here with these congresses, any more than with the national societies relative to special sciences. In my book on the study of the history of mathematics, I shall speak of the mathematical societies and congresses. However, this is the proper place to speak of two other series of international congresses which concern the history and philosophy of science in general; these are the congresses of history and philosophy.

In addition to two international meetings — at Chicago, 1893, and The Hague, 1898 — which are not counted in the regular series, the international congresses of historical sciences have taken place as follows:

    I. Paris, 1900.
    II. Rome, 1903.
    III. Berlin, 1908.
    IV. London, 1913.
    V. Brussels, 1923.
    VI. Oslo, 1928.
    VII. Warsaw, 1933.

The international congresses of philosophy have met as follows:

    I. Paris, 1900.
    II. Geneva, 1904.
    III. Heidelberg, 1908.
    IV. Bologna, 1911.
    V. Naples, 1924.
    VI. Cambridge, Mass., 1926.
    VII. Oxford, 1930.
    VIII. Prague, 1934.

The proceedings of these congresses, especially of the philosophical ones, contain valuable materials for the historians of science. For example, Paul Tannery took a leading part in the historical congress of

[1] No meetings took place in 1914, 1915, 1918, 1920, 1922.

Rome (1903) and in the philosophical congresses of Paris (1900) and Geneva (1904). The special section under his chairmanship of the Geneva meeting was perhaps the most brilliant congress of the history of science which ever occurred.

An international congress of scientific philosophy, the first of its kind,[1] took place in Paris, September, 1935; a second meeting will take place in Copenhagen 1936.

To conclude, mention must be made of the International Congresses of the History of Science organized by the Academy *ad hoc*. Three congresses have thus far taken place:

I. Paris, 1929.
II. London, 1931.
III. Coimbra, 1934.

and the following are in preparation:

IV. Prague, 1937.
V. Lausanne, 1940.

No proceedings have been published of the first two congresses, except for summaries which appeared in *Archeion* and *Isis*, and the publication of individual papers in various journals. For the third one, see Actes, conférences et communications du 111e Congrès international d'histoire des sciences (Lisbon 1935). It is expected that these congresses will become gradually more and more important, because the problems interesting historians of science are generally too technical to interest conventional historians, and too concrete and limited to interest conventional philosophers.

---

[1] Yet every congress of philosophy has been also, through one of its sections, a congress of scientific philosophy. Philosophers are generally far more interested in the philosophy than in the history of science, and there seems to be less justification for the organization of special congresses for the philosophy than for the history of science.

INDEX

INDEX

I. PERSONS

II. TITLES OF JOURNALS, SERIALS, AND INSTITUTIONS

FOUNDATIONS OF SCIENCE:
THE PHILOSOPHY OF THEORY AND EXPERIMENT
by N. R. Campbell

In this volume, formerly entitled PHYSICS: THE ELEMENTS, Dr. Campbell provides a critique of the most fundamental concepts of science in general and of physics in particular. His point of view is that of the experimental physicist rather than the mathematician. This, combined with his knowledge of the entire field of physics, allows his investigation to proceed along unique lines.

This book has three purposes. (1) To discover why certain propositions of science are accepted without question. These include the use of hypothesis and theory, induction, application of "numbers" to phenomena, dimensional analysis, etc. (2) To demarcate science from philosophy, and to discuss attempts to make one a branch of the other. (3) To clarify our understanding of the tools of science (theory, probability, measurement), to prevent errors in their use, and to extend our understanding of the phenomena which we investigate by their means. The author draws upon the work of countless predecessors, ranging from Euclid and Aristotle to Maxwell, Planck, Poincaré, Bergson, and scores of others.

This is not an elementary work. It is written for the reader who has a good background in the physical sciences and it has been accepted as a classic in its field. It is difficult to conceive that anyone interested in the sciences would not profit by studying this monumental work.

FOUNDATIONS OF SCIENCE is divided into two parts. The first part analyzes the presuppositions upon which scientific thought is based. Subject matter of science; the nature, discovery, proof of laws; theories; chance and probability; science and philosophy are discussed, and the physical nature of the world is studied in relation to problems suggested by mechanics, thermodynamics, gas theory, and electrical phenomena. In the second part the author covers the nature of experiment and the application of mathematics; measurement, magnitudes, fractional and negative, units and dimensions; errors of measurement etc. are all considered. An appendix covers problems that arise from relativity, force, motion, space & time.

Index. xii + 565pp. 5⅜ x 8.

S372 Paperbound $2.95

SCIENCE AND METHOD
by Henri Poincare

Written by Henri Poincare, who has been termed the last mathematical universalist and the greatest mathematician since Gauss, this volume is concerned with the basic methodology and psychology of scientific discovery, especially in mathematics and mathematical physics. It explains how the scientist analyzes and selects facts with which he must work, and analyzes the nature of experimentation, theory, and the human mind, as they are applied to the acquisition of organized knowledge.

Examples from many fields of science illustrate Poincare's discussion of the germination of ideas. Besides special topics, this volume also contains Poincare's famous discussion of his own idea-creating mental processes, and the use of the unconscious mind. Especially valuable for the modern mathematician or logician is a searching examination of the ideas of Whitehead, Hilbert, and Russell.

"Vivid . . . immense clarity . . .. the product of a brilliant and extremely forceful intellect," JOURNAL OF THE ROYAL NAVAL SCIENTIFIC SERVICE. "Still a sheer joy to read," MATHEMATICAL GAZETTE. "Should be read by any student, teacher or researcher in mathematics," MATHEMATICS TEACHER.

Translated by Francis Maitland. 288pp.

S222 Paperbound **$1.25**

A CONCISE HISTORY OF MATHEMATICS

by D. J. Struik

This compact, readable history describes the main trends in the development of all fields of mathematics throughout the ages, Students, researchers, historians—specialists and laymen alike—will find it extremely useful and interesting.

Beginning with the Ancient Near East, the author traces mathematical ideas and techniques through Egypt, Babylonia, China, India, and Arabia. He considers Greek and Roman developments from their beginnings in Ionian rationalism to the fall of Constantinople; covers Medieval European ideas and Renaissance trends; analyzes 17th and 18th century contributions; and concludes with an exposition of 19th century concepts.

A CONCISE HISTORY OF MATHEMATICS covers such early developments as the Egyptian Papyrus Rhind, the Ten Classics of China, the Siddhantas of India, the Liber Abaci, and others. Every important figure in mathematical history is dealt with—Euclid, Archimedes, Diophantus, Omar Khayyam, Boethius, Fermat, Pascal, Newton, Leibnitz, Fourier, Gauss, Riemann, Cantor, and many others.

"A very valuable book," AMERICAN MATHEMATICAL MONTHLY. "A remarkably complete and accurate picture of the history of pure mathematics," JOURNAL OF THE ROYAL NAVAL SCIENTIFIC SERVICE. "Compact, orderly, authentic," AMERICAN JOURNAL OF PSYCHOLOGY.

Second revised edition. Bibliography. Index. 60 illustrations, including Egyptian papyri, Greek mss., portraits of 31 eminent mathematicians. xix + 299pp. 5⅜ x 8.

S255　Paperbound　**$1.75**

THE GEOMETRY OF RENÉ DESCARTES

This is an unabridged republication of the definitive English translation of one of the very greatest classics of science. Originally
published in 1637, it has been characterized as "the greatest single
step ever made in the progress of the exact sciences" (John Stuart
Mill); as a book which "remade geometry and made modern geometry
possible," (Eric Temple Bell). It "revolutionized the entire conception
of the object of mathematical science," (J. Hadamard).

With this volume Descartes founded modern analytical geometry.
Reducing geometry to algebra and analysis, and conversely showing
that analysis may be translated into geometry, it opened the way
for modern mathematics. Descartes was the first to classify curves
systematically, and to demonstrate algebraic solution of geometric
curves. His geometric interpretation of negative quantities led to
later concepts of continuity and the theory of function. The third
book contains important contributions to the theory of equations.

This edition contains the entire definitive Smith-Latham translation
of Descartes's three books: **Problems the Construction of which Requires
Only Straight Lines and Circles; On the Nature of Curved Lines; On
the Construction of Solid or Supersolid Problems.** Interleaved page
by page with the translation is a complete facsimile of the 1637
French text, together with all Descartes's original illustrations. 248
footnotes explain the text and add further bibliography.

Translated by David E. Smith and Marcia L. Latham. Preface. Index.
50 figures. xiii+244pp. 5⅜ x 8.   S68 Paperbound $1.50